The
Healing Power
of
Forgiveness

by
Sharon Platt-McDonald
MSc, RHV, RM, RGN

About the author

Sharon Platt-McDonald is a health professional. Her strategic role entails developing health programmes and resources, and the presentation of health seminars. She regularly writes for publications both nationally and internationally.

The
Healing Power
of
Forgiveness

by
Sharon Platt-McDonald
MSc, RHV, RM, RGN

'Be gentle and forbearing with one another and, if one has a
difference (a grievance or complaint) against another,
readily pardoning each other; even as the Lord has
[freely] forgiven you, so must you also [forgive].'
Colossians 3:13 (Amplified Bible)

The Healing Power of Forgiveness

Contents

Contents

The Healing Power of Forgiveness

Acknowledgements

There are many people whom I would like to acknowledge in assisting with the publication of this book. Firstly to the Stanborough Press editorial and design team who turned my manuscript into this book. Secondly, to the many friends, colleagues and clients who have encouraged me to write a book on forgiveness following the various workshops I have conducted on the subject over the years. Thank you for making this vision a reality.

This book is dedicated to my mother, truly a virtuous woman, who taught me the principles of forgiveness. She has been my mentor, role model and inspiration. I am also grateful to the many others who have enhanced my understanding of forgiveness through the years. Most of all, my thanks to God, who daily reminds us that forgiveness is possible.

'Forgiveness is the process of reframing one's anger and hurt from the past, with the goal of recovering one's peace in the present and revitalising one's purpose and hopes for the future.' Dr Dick Tibbits *(Forgive to Live)*

Another book on forgiveness?

Most Christian bookshops will have at least one book in stock on forgiveness. In fact, all the major world religions have something to say about the subject. I have read a number of books on forgiveness and maybe you have too. So what makes this one any different?

Motivated by the *Forgiveness as Healing* workshops that I have conducted over the years, I recognised the need for a holistic approach to forgiveness and the healing it provides for the whole person – physically, emotionally, spiritually and socially. I saw that it was important to make people conscious of the wider implications of forgiveness and how it impacts all aspects of our lives. Additionally, I sensed the importance of having a set of 'reflection points' at the end of each chapter. This would give readers an opportunity to think through what they have just read and make a personal application of it. These are followed up by 'action' segments which assist them to implement key aspects of the chapter or any specific recommendations that they may find helpful.

Knowing the usefulness of case studies in the learning process, I wanted the book to show how real people coped with forgiveness in their lives. For this reason I have included the incredible stories of Michael (a Jew) and Larry (a former Ku Klux Klan member) and what brought them together; of 'Phil and Julia' as they share their story of reconciliation following a challenging period during their marriage; and of Anne, who, through the loss of family members during the conflict in

The Healing Power of Forgiveness

Ireland, turned her pain into productivity. I wanted readers to share the deeply moving account of Alice and Emmanuel as they share their perspectives as victim and perpetrator during the Rwandan genocide; and to reflect on the selflessness of Elizabeth – a missionary – who demonstrates true forgiveness by taking a bold step to meet with those who had caused her deep personal pain.

In the chapter on research we specifically examine the reports from scientists which demonstrate the harmful effects of choosing not to forgive and of holding on to resentments. We analyse the work of researchers and the data they have presented which suggest that failure to forgive can, over a lifetime, raise a person's risk for heart disease, mental illness and other debilitating illnesses.[1]

As you read you will come across some studies that suggest that forgiveness actually improves health, causing positive physiological, emotional and behavioural benefits. You will also notice that there is much data that shows the correlation between good lifestyle habits and how to build emotional resilience.

Draw your own conclusion as you review the research suggesting that, just as we can successfully learn how to apply proper diet and exercise to enhance our well-being, so we can learn how to forgive in a way that preserves health and prevents disease. By the final chapter, I hope you will agree that forgiveness is truly a prescription for healing our wounded hearts and minds from the hurts and injuries they encounter when others do us wrong.

Although I share research data and case studies about individuals whose forgiveness journey we can applaud, the greatest lesson and story of forgiveness for me was displayed on the cross. When Jesus suffered in our place and died for our sins, bearing the assaults of injustice heaped upon Him by His persecutors, in the midst of His extreme pain and suffering He prayed for those who harmed Him. The words recorded in Luke 23:34 – *'Father forgive them, for they know not what they do . . .'* – were not only a prayer for forgiveness for those who crucified Him, but also a plea to all humanity. His example of extending grace to those who sought Him harm is truly the ultimate example of forgiveness.

So, reader, accept the healing prescription that forgiveness brings as you let go of resentment, bitterness and the desire for revenge towards those who have hurt you. Ask God to apply His healing touch to all the areas where you hurt. In doing so, you will be able to release the pain of the past, bring freedom to your present circumstances and enthusiastically embrace the future God has in store for you.

So let's begin.

The Healing Power of Forgiveness

The journey begins:
A personal reflection

Most of us know that forgiveness is easier to talk about than to practise.

C. S. Lewis said: 'Everyone says forgiveness is a lovely idea until they have something to forgive.'[2]

Until I experienced the negative side effects of holding on to unforgiveness, the idea of forgiveness was something I was acquainted with on a cognitive level. Oh, I knew about it as a spiritual principle and one that I should aspire to as a Christian, but over the past decades I have had many experiences that have tested my willingness to forgive.

Here's one example.

While at work one busy afternoon, I received an email that set me off in negative mode. The email commenced with a remark heavy with sarcasm, and was followed by an accusation that was completely unfounded. Shocked and angry, my fingers flew over the keyboard in an anxious attempt to put the matter right and bring the individual up to date with the truth. As I typed furiously (not pausing to correct mistakes) I realised my hands were shaking. I was very upset. I found myself asking a barrage of questions, 'How could someone in that position say such mean and false things?' 'Why do people seek to inflict hurt on others without any care for their feelings?' 'How was it possible for them to come to such a negative conclusion?' What a cheek! How cruel and unnecessary! My mind was racing with questions and other comments as I battered the keys in reply at a speed I was not accustomed to (hence the grammatical errors). I was in the grip of anger.

At first, I had not realised how deeply wounded I was by the email. It was not until several weeks later when recounting the incident to friends and family that I realised how much of a negative impact the incident had on me. As I described how upset it had made me, I felt the same agitation coming to the fore again, just as acutely as it had when I first read the email. As I recounted the incident to my sisters my speech became rapid and increased in volume, and I paced back and forth getting myself upset all over again.

Concerned by my level of agitation, my youngest sister gently tapped me on the hand (in an attempt to calm me down) and informed me that I was behaving as if the incident had just happened, and as if I were talking directly to the offender and 'telling him or her off'. She then drew up a chair, sat me down and offered me a glass of water. At that moment I felt my whole body relax and my heart rate began to slow down. As I became calmer, I reflected on what had just happened, examining both my physiological and emotional responses. Although I knew that I needed to 'let go' of this hurt in order to move on, I rationalised that my pain was justified so somehow it felt reasonable to hang on to the memory. I felt ashamed of my behaviour.

The turning point, however, came several weeks later as I thought about a comment one of my sisters had made after she listened to my account of the incident. She stated that, although it was clear that I had been wronged, I was prolonging the agony of the experience by holding on to the hurt I was feeling. This I knew to be true, yet I had wanted to hold on to that memory as a way of getting back at the individual whom I did not want to confront about the hurt I was feeling. By doing this, I felt I was holding the person to account for his/her actions. I rationalised that if I just dismissed the incident the person would somehow be 'let off the hook'.

Finally, the realisation hit home that this was not so much about giving up the 'right' to be angry, as it was about my choice to remain angry. The fact was that holding on to the memory and its associated pain was making me unhappy; and that was not where I wanted to be. I had to ask myself the question: what was I gaining by not letting go? I came to the swift conclusion that the only thing that I was adding to the experience was resentment and ongoing hurt.

My first step in the forgiveness process was to realise that my life was bigger than that single incident. It did not define my existence. I then had to decide what I wanted to do with the memory and how I would react each time it came to mind. If I wanted to be relieved of the hurt and not continue to feel resentful, I would need to think differently about the individual. I realised that I was focusing more on the individual instead of my reaction, and the choice I had in deciding how I would respond. So instead of the negative thoughts I would have whenever I was reminded of the person, I thought rather of how to temper my response.

As a Christian my faith also played a part in the process. I asked for God's help in letting go and moving on. I made a conscious effort to mention the individual's name in my prayers and asked God to help me be forgiving – not to bear a grudge against the person. It was not long before I forgot about the incident completely. Whenever the individual's name was mentioned after that, I no longer felt upset. My healing had begun; I was now at peace.

Forgiveness steps

The key forgiveness steps I learnt were these:
- The first step was to learn to 'retell' my account of the incident. This meant that I no longer talked about it in the

same negative way. Initially I found this a little challenging as I could not find anything positive about the contents of the email that had been sent to me. I felt that by describing the details I would simply be stating the 'facts'. However, when I took some time to think about the event and recall my story, instead of adding the emotions of anger, bitterness and all the negative feelings I associated with the email (which would reinforce the pain), I talked instead about the facts and not the associated feelings.

• I then put the incident into perspective by accepting that it was in the past and that I needed to leave it there. In fact, when I really thought about it, I realised that it was not that big a deal anyway, and certainly not significant enough to let it negatively impact the present, let alone my future.

Reflection:

• Retelling my account of the incident without reinforcing the associated negative emotions helped to release me from those past 'hurtful' memories – I was no longer tied to the past. Additionally, it helped to adjust the picture I had held in my mind about the incident. In turn, this helped to diminish the significance I attributed to the event. Finally, this made the act of 'letting it go' more achievable.

The Healing Power of Forgiveness

A forgiveness story to get started

> 'We win by tenderness; we conquer by forgiveness.'
> Frederick William Robertson

A powerful story, exemplifying the power of forgiveness and love, is that of Michael Weisser, a Jew and cantor at a Reform synagogue in Lincoln, Nebraska. Shortly after moving to Lincoln he began receiving harassing phone calls. The abusive phone calls came from Larry Trapp, a Neo-Nazi and Grand Dragon of the White Knights of the Ku Klux Klan, who sought to intimidate and drive Weisser out of the neighbourhood.

Due to the debilitating effects of diabetes, Larry Trapp had lost both legs and was confined to a wheelchair. In addition to his physical challenges, Larry's own father had ridiculed him for his disabilities. This had made Larry very bitter. In turn, he vented his anger on the Jew, Michael Weisser.

Growing weary of the harassing phone calls, Michael decided to fight back. While answering one of Larry's phone calls, he confronted him with this statement. 'You know, Larry, with your physical disabilities, the Nazis would have made you the first to die. I hope you also know that one day you will have to answer for all this hatred.'

Larry was left to think about what Michael had said. Shortly afterwards Larry phoned Michael. This time, however, there were no racist slogans, threats or Neo-Nazi comments. Instead of a hateful verbal attack, Larry just wanted to talk. How many calls ensued after that we are not told, but slowly a relationship began to build between the two men. Amazingly, the Weisser family began to open up their hearts to Larry. Realising that there were tasks he found difficult, they assisted him to meet these needs.

They did his shopping, cared for him, visited him and showed him genuine love. Eventually, Larry stripped away the armour of hate that he had embraced for so long, gave away his weapons and resigned from the Klan.

Larry took the step to learn more about the people he had despised for so long. He was particularly interested in how they had survived centuries of irrational hate and abuse. It was Michael who gave him the information he searched for, filling in all the gaps. Nine months later Larry, ex-Klan member, made an extraordinary decision to convert to Judaism and became a member of the Reformed congregation for which Michael was cantor.

When Larry became too weak to care for himself it was the Weissers who took him into their home and cared for him, as if he were a family member. Michael's wife Julie, a nurse, made the dramatic decision to resign from her job in order to care for Larry. In an act of appreciation Larry ordered flowers for Julie, and with the bouquet there was a note attached which read: 'Thank you for changing me from a dragon to a butterfly.'

Several months later, in September, 1992, when Larry died, he was surrounded by the Weisser family who had lovingly taken him in. At his funeral, he was eulogised by a black activist, Donna Polk, whom he had previously harassed. Among the moving words she shared were these – 'One never knows what love will do to ignite the spark of the truly human in a very mean world.'[3]

The Healing Power of Forgiveness

Reflection:

- Have you ever tried to be kind to someone who disliked you? What did it feel like?
- Have you tried to love someone, only to find them throwing hate back at you?
- Remember that where love and hate come face to face, there will always be tension as one tries to triumph over the other. The biblical directive that guides us under such circumstances is: '. . . overcome evil with good' (Romans 12:21).

Action:

- Think of someone who may have been unkind to you. Write his or her name down and pray over that name every day in your prayer time. Ask God to give you the willingness to begin the forgiveness journey so that you can move forward.

A look at forgiveness

The Oxford dictionaries define the word 'forgive' as follows: to 'stop feeling angry or resentful towards (someone) for an offence, flaw, or mistake' and no longer 'wish to punish'.[4]

In Dr Dick Tibbits' workbook on the Forgive to Live programme that he runs he defines forgiveness like this:

'Forgiveness is the process of reframing one's anger and hurt from the past, with the goal of recovering one's peace in the present and revitalising one's purpose and hopes for the future.'[5]

What a great description, and one that we can all aspire to in our desire to truly experience forgiveness, both for ourselves and for others. It is important to note though, that forgiveness is a journey – and, as such, it takes time for the healing to occur. This is a concept that will emerge as we go through the various chapters in this book.

We are taught that we should forgive. It is a biblical directive and we know it is the right thing to do. However, the 'how to' and actual 'experience' of forgiving can be a challenging process. Over the years of presenting on the subject of forgiveness I have had the opportunity to dialogue with several individuals about their experiences of forgiveness. Many were surprised that the act of forgiving was more painful than they had anticipated, and that, in many instances, the pain lingered a lot longer than they had thought possible. It was clear that the journey to forgiveness was not always easy or straightforward.

However, the most poignant discovery for many was the

The Healing Power of Forgiveness

healing they actually experienced when they finally forgave, and the peace that came when they 'released' the issue or individual which caused them pain and handed the situation over completely to God. It was from that point that they began to experience restoration. It is this message of restoration and healing, which comes from forgiving and accepting forgiveness, that I wish to share in this little volume.

Historically, forgiveness has been at the heart of the teachings of the major world religions. In addition, empirical research from clinical and social psychologists, medical practitioners and other researchers is producing evidence demonstrating the link between the emotions and heart health.

Psychologist Fred Luskin, director of Stanford University's Forgiveness Projects and a leading researcher in this area, states: 'Who would have thought it – something locked away in religious culture could be turned into a secular training programme . . . it's a skill that can be taught.'[6]

I trust that as you read through this book, it will inspire you to think about the power of forgiveness. As you share in the accounts of individuals who have been challenged to forgive in spite of the traumatic experiences they have encountered, try to recall a bitter life experience that you have encountered. As you do so, maybe you could think about and apply the 'reflection' and 'action' segments as a prescription for the hurts of the past, the challenges of the present and the fears for the future, in order to bring healing, wholeness and hope.

Reflection:

- What is causing you hurt?
- What negative life experience has happened to you for which you are holding others responsible?
- What is happening to you currently for which you may be blaming yourself, or can't forgive yourself?

- What has happened in your life for which you may even be blaming God and holding resentment against Him because you perceived that He allowed you to go through difficult life circumstances?

I hope some of these questions will be answered as you read the ensuing chapters.

Action:

- Take some time to reflect on the questions above and write down the thoughts that come to you as you answer each one.

The Healing Power of Forgiveness

In thinking about the process of forgiveness and the questions we sometimes ask ourselves about our ability to forgive, I devised the diagrams in this section to highlight key messages.

Why the need to forgive?

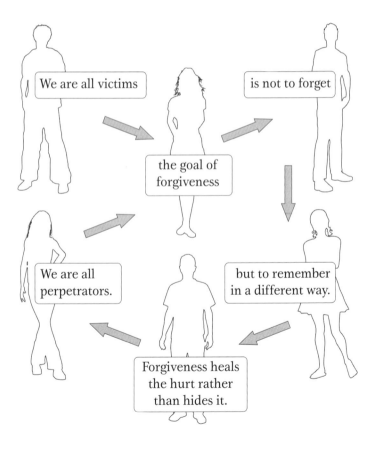

We are all victims

is not to forget

the goal of forgiveness

We are all perpetrators.

but to remember in a different way.

Forgiveness heals the hurt rather than hides it.

Why do I need to forgive?

In answering the question the following pointers may be helpful:

- Forgiveness is generally defined as giving up the resentment, anger or hurt resulting from a perceived offence against you, and ceasing to demand punishment or restitution for it.
- With every forgiveness story there is a victim and a perpetrator. A closer look at the issues involved, and at our lives in general, will highlight that at some time or other we have all been perpetrators in some way. The Bible states: '. . . all have sinned and fall short of the glory of God' (Romans 3:23).
- If God can forgive each of us for our transgressions we can also forgive others for theirs.
- The greatest power you have over anyone who has hurt you is the power of forgiveness.
- When you say to the person who has hurt you, 'I forgive you and no longer hold it against you', you have loosened the negative bond that exists between you.
- Forgiveness could be referred to as the elimination of all desire for revenge against those who have hurt us deeply.
- This elimination usually brings an *inner peace* and the *freedom* of *not* having our lives defined by the injuries we have suffered.
- By doing this you free yourself from the 'burden' of being the 'offended one'. It liberates both parties.
- Forgiveness allows you to live in the present and leave the past behind.
- When we don't forgive those who have wounded us, we constantly carry them in our thoughts, or worse, like a millstone around our necks.
- When you nurse a hurt you feed it. You make it grow until

The Healing Power of Forgiveness

it preoccupies your thoughts and impacts your life in a negative way.

- While you cannot automatically forget a hurtful incident because the brain stores the memory of such experiences, forgiveness changes the way we remember. We recall the event from a different perspective, and as time progresses we recall the incident but the associated pain is no longer there.
- Although the decision to forgive may be immediate, the healing process may take time. This is one reason why forgiveness is often referred to as a journey.
- Many people are trapped in the bondage of unforgiveness. Look at the following diagram and think about it with regard to harbouring an unforgiving attitude.

Lack of forgiveness leads to:

Negative thinking

Negative feelings

Negative actions

Negative speaking

What if I cannot forgive him/her?

If you tell yourself you are unable to forgive you are effectively causing the following to happen:

- Not forgiving someone the hurt they have caused you is like picking up a heavy burden each day and carrying it around with you wherever you go.
- By carrying a grudge you enable the offender to keep hurting you.
- The negative feelings we harbour when we fail to forgive will eventually lead to negative behaviour, which will be reflected in our thoughts, words and actions.
- When we hold on to unforgiveness it leads to unresolved negative emotions. These can also present themselves as physiological ailments such as raised blood pressure, increased heart rate, tensed muscles and other stress-related problems.[7]

Many scientific studies point to the detrimental physiological, emotional, social and spiritual effects a lack of forgiveness can have.[8]

Am I supposed to forget as well as forgive?

- It is impossible to truly forget wrongs that have been committed against us, because we cannot selectively 'delete' events from our memory.
- The brain is like a computer – it absorbs data put into it through its neurological 'wiring' (neurons) and stores it on the 'hard drive' (network of interconnected neurons), which is technically like a computer's memory.
- It is clear, then, that we are biologically wired to remember.
- Forgiveness does not necessarily involve a literal forgetting. Forgetting may not be a realistic or desirable goal. Forgiveness involves remembering in a different way.

The Healing Power of Forgiveness

This happens when you recall the incident but the associated pain is no longer there with the same intensity as before. This remembering or reliving may initially include much of the original pain, the feelings of resentment and the desire to 'get even'.

- Despite the familiar cliché, 'forgive and forget', most of us find forgetting nearly impossible. Although we may claim to have forgiven someone, the memory of what they did may haunt us for a long time.
- However, by 'reframing', or repackaging the experience differently (retelling the story in a different way), you recall the memory from a different perspective, which enables you to see the whole picture, the circumstances surrounding the issue, and not just the offending person or what he/she has done to you. As a result we remember 'differently' and the act of remembering becomes more wholesome.
- You are then able to begin letting go of the hold that person has on your life and move away from constantly thinking about them and what they have done to you.
- I would say forgive and 'forget' (leave behind) the desire to get even or take revenge, the entitlement to be right, and the relentless expectation that the perpetrator must get their just reward.

How do I learn how to forgive?

As you contemplate this question and the possible responses, take time to analyse the following:

- You can create conditions where forgiveness is more likely to occur. Begin by changing your mindset.
- Remember that because of our imperfect natures every one of us, at some point in our lives, has caused hurt to others, whether it was intentional or not. Therefore we too need forgiveness.

- Refusing to replay the hurtful incident over and over again may help you to move on from the past.
- Forgiveness does not mean that you condone the wrong done against you, or deny it, pretending that it never happened.
- We forgive by acknowledging the wrong that has been done to us.
- As we forgive others we must acknowledge that we are also perpetrators.
- We forgive by forfeiting our 'injury story' and the self-pity we attach to it. This enables us to see things from a more objective and healthy perspective, which enables us to move on from the hurt.
- We forgive others as we have been forgiven by God.
- We forgive unconditionally when we remember God's unconditional love for us and His forgiveness of our sins on a daily basis.
- We forgive in full or not at all.

A step forward

In contemplating your decision to forgive and the practical steps you will take to achieve this, it is useful to bear the following points in mind:

- Begin by telling yourself that forgiveness is possible.
- Accept that your decision to forgive may not result in a major change in the other person.
- Understand that when you forgive, the pain may not go away entirely. It is the desire for revenge that is no longer there.
- Ask God to heal your hurts.
- Change your 'injury story'. This will enable you to move from being a victim to appearing more like a survivor who is full of hope.

The Healing Power of Forgiveness

- The ultimate goal, however, is emotional healing in which negative emotions such as resentment, bitterness, hostility, hatred, anger, and fear are replaced with love, compassion, sympathy, and empathy.
- You can tell yourself, 'I am not going to seek revenge.'
- Forgiveness can bring peace to conflict situations, both for the 'forgiver' and for the 'forgiven'. It has potential to bring about healing and reconciliation.
- Access useful resources on forgiveness to assist you, such as Dr Tibbits' 'Forgive to Live' programme (*www.ForgiveToLive.net*), Frederick Luskin's book *Forgive for Good* or Dr Robert Enright's book *Forgiveness is a Choice – A Step-by-Step Process for Resolving Anger and Restoring Hope*.
- By applying the aforementioned points, a number of people I have worked with over the past years have been able to move forward with their lives and experience release from years of unforgiveness. It begins with one step, and moves forward one step at a time.

Forgiveness at close range

At some point, each of us has brought hurt into the lives of others, whether we meant to or not. As fallible humans we all fall short in some way and this often causes pain to ourselves as well as others. However, when our actions or the actions of others cause hurt to those closest to us or even to ourselves, some have found that the pain is sometimes more pronounced. This may be because of the emotional connection and bond we have with them, and the fact that we expect more of those we know well and are connected to in some way. Therefore when they 'fail' us the disappointment is felt more deeply than if they were strangers or casual acquaintances.

When those closest to us hurt our feelings or their actions cause us significant harm, the process of forgiveness can be a challenge as we question how someone so close to us can hurt us so deeply.

Some time ago, I sat with a couple who shared the story of their journey to forgiveness after trust broke down in their marital relationship. Here is their story, which they have given me permission to tell. Their names have been changed to protect their identity.

Phil and Julia's story

Phil and Julia had been married for seven years. They prided themselves on what they called a 'good marriage' – one based on a close friendship between them. However, just after their seventh anniversary Phil began to review his life goals and started to experience negative self-talk about what he had not accomplished in life. Realising that he was soon to turn fifty, he evaluated his achievements over the years and felt that he had not accomplished much and did not see how he was going to make up for what he called 'lost time'. He would occasionally share these thoughts with Julia, but the more she encouraged him and tried to point out how well he had done, the more he just failed to find anything good in his life to celebrate, and his self-esteem began to suffer.

By comparison with a number of his friends, Phil was employed in what he referred to as a 'low-paid, dead-end job'. For years he had tried to share some of his innovative ideas with the company, but when they did not take up his suggestions he felt resentful. A handful of individuals had been promoted over the years, but Phil had been 'passed over' as he put it, and now there were no more vacancies or other available positions to move up into. He had retrained at evening classes to gain new skills in order to boost his chances of diversifying into a new career. However, his attempts to move on seemed futile as he was unsuccessful with interviews for jobs in the area in which he had retrained. He was repeatedly told that he did not have the experience they required. This caused Phil's self-esteem to plummet even further.

To make matters worse, his wife Julia had received a number of promotions over the years and had now moved on to an executive role in a major company, where her salary was more than twice his own. Seeking to dull the pain he was feeling, Phil began surfing the internet. He would 'lose' himself for hours in an attempt to divert the increasingly low moods he was experiencing. He found himself hooked on the various chat lines and websites where 'interesting' women made him feel younger, wanted and important. He had adopted a pseudo-name and passed himself off as a successful business executive who was looking for friendship.

As time went on Phil lost interest in church activities and began missing church services, saying that God was no longer listening to him. His interest in Julia waned and she would sometimes cry herself to sleep as he became more and more distant. Julia became concerned about his emotional stability as his personality had changed so drastically. Once when they were talking he had mentioned that he felt as though he was 'losing it mentally'. Julia often wondered about the many hours he spent on the internet and who it was he was talking with. Additionally, after these lengthy internet sessions he always seemed disconnected and cold towards her.

Julia tried to address the issue and the change it was bringing about in their marriage. However, every time she brought the subject up he became very defensive. Phil denied that anything untoward was going on. Nevertheless, after several internet relationships Phil became deeply connected to one particular woman and soon they started planning their meeting.

It was at this point that Julia found out what Phil had been doing. One night when she awoke with a cough and went to get linctus from the medicine cupboard, she heard Phil talking and laughing in the office. On entering the room she found Phil talking on his webcam to a scantily clad woman. Needless to say the tight relationship that Phil and Julia had once enjoyed became very strained, and bitter arguments ensued. Phil suggested that maybe it was best that he left. He said he no longer felt connected to Julia in the way that he did with some of the women online.

The shock of the discovery created an emotional strain for Julia, and the trauma she experienced as a result caused her to develop panic attacks. In addition, she developed asthmatic symptoms and was diagnosed with bronchial asthma, which necessitated medical intervention. Her doctor informed her she would require long-term monitoring and medication. She lost confidence in herself, and became fretful and anxious each time she saw her husband speaking with other women on the rare occasions that they went out together. She wondered whether she would ever be able to trust Phil again.

In an attempt to save their marriage Julia suggested that both she and Phil attend a marriage counselling series with a Christian counsellor. Phil stepped down from his position at church over his bitterness towards God, and the neglect of his Christian values and faith through his increasing involvement in these internet relationships. It was only at the point of their counselling sessions that they both realised that Phil had been experiencing a mid-life crisis. It also became evident that he had become addicted to the chat-lines and required professional help to assist him in overcoming this. Julia took some time off from work and adjusted her schedule to spend more time with Phil. However, she became resentful that she was adapting her life to try and compensate for Phil's wrongdoing.

Julia reports that the road to forgiveness was hard, because each time she had a panic or asthma attack she would blame Phil for her condition. As she had never had asthma as a child or any previous episodes of panic disorder, her GP had suggested that maybe the sudden onset of asthma and the panic attacks were linked to severe stress. Her hair had also begun to fall out and she began suffering from insomnia. It made Julia cross when most nights she lay in bed awake while Phil was deeply asleep, snoring beside her. She felt anger towards him. He was the reason for her sleeplessness due to the trauma he had put her through, and yet he was able to sleep soundly at night – and, unlike her, had no medical conditions to worry about.

Both Julia and Phil recognised that it was more than the issue of Phil's past behaviour that they had to cope with. It was now also Julia's resentment of Phil that was negatively impacting their marriage. She felt justified in her resentment because she felt that Phil had not shown the necessary remorse for his actions and her subsequent ill health. This caused Phil to feel angry that Julia was holding his past against him, and he felt it was time for her to move on so things could get back to normal again. Julia then became upset with Phil because she felt he was rushing her healing. In fact, she felt aggrieved that each time she mentioned that she was still feeling hurt by his behaviour and the impact it had had on her health, he would accuse her of making herself ill by not forgiving.

The subject of forgiveness became a contentious issue. Phil held to the view that their marriage was deteriorating because Julia refused to forgive. Julia, however, felt their marriage was shaky because Phil had not expressed remorse for what he had done and the pain it had caused her, meaning that he had not repented of his actions. She felt this to be true particularly as Phil continued to connect to social networks and occasionally went back to the chat-lines. Julia had always held the view that if someone did not confess their fault and apologise to the individual they hurt then the injured party was not bound to forgive. And so, the feud continued between them.

Eventually, through the support of family and prayer partners, both Phil and Julia began to heal.

It took a process of nearly two years to restore their relationship and for Phil to no longer feel the need to seek the affirmation of other women on chat-lines. Recommitting himself to God, Phil was able to allow God to rebuild his self-esteem, and his trust and faith in God grew. Julia has learnt the pain of what holding on to resentment can do. She has now learned to cope with her health challenges and each time she becomes unwell, instead of blaming Phil, she asks God for strength to manage her health. Today Phil reports that, emotionally, he is stronger than ever, is reconnected with his wife, and is looking forward to the next fifty years, whatever they may bring.

Forgiveness steps:

Speaking about the steps she took to arrive at forgiveness, Julia identified the following as key factors:

1. Look beyond the person who has hurt you. Without excusing what they have done, very often you will find that they have a problem and may be in need of help. In Julia's case her husband was replicating what he had encountered growing up as a child.

2. Acknowledge the pain and hurt you feel as a natural response to being injured. However, you also need to acknowledge the impact of nursing a grudge and how it may be affecting your well-being. Ask yourself what the benefit would be of holding on to the feeling of hurt.

3. Recognise that you may require help to cope with the painful memories. In Julia's case, she eventually sought counselling as a way of unpacking the painful episode, confronting her feelings, seeking healthy expressions for her anger and laying the bitterness to rest. She also turned to her faith to help her. Praying to God on a daily basis enabled her to feel 'uplifted' and that she was not alone.

4. Specifically praying for the desire to forgive was challenging, because she had felt for so long that he needed to be punished for what he had inflicted on her. However, when she persevered in asking for the strength to be able to forgive, it became evident that the more she did so, the less she thought about her hurt, and in doing so she realised that she was slowly letting go of the past.

Reflection:

- We need to forgive those closest to us who have offended us if we are to prevent the breakdown of meaningful relationships.
- When the reminders of someone's wrongdoing face you every day, such as poor health conditions, poverty, physical injury, disability or depression, how can you move past this 'evidence' to a place of forgiveness?
- Think of a family member who has caused you hurt and whose actions are still negatively impacting your life in some way. Think of how you are currently dealing with that memory and if your hurt is currently holding you back from experiencing some level of peace and joy. Ask God to help you heal. If you are struggling to forgive the issues that have caused your pain, then Christian counselling may be advisable, as well as the use of resources like Dr Dick Tibbits' Forgive to Live programme (*www.ForgiveToLive.net*).

Action:

- If you have been disappointed by the betrayal, hurt or abuse of a family member or of individuals close to you, tell God exactly how you are feeling and the struggle you are experiencing to forgive them.
- Partner in prayer with someone whom you trust, and agree to pray together that God will release any bitterness you may be holding for the individual who offended you and give you the power to forgive them for what they have done.
- If you feel traumatised by what has happened to you it may be necessary to seek professional help and Christian counselling.

The Healing Power of Forgiveness

- Organisations like the Counselling & Prayer Trust (020 7384 9212) or RELATE (0300 100 1234); *enquiries@relate.org.uk*; may be helpful under the circumstances.

Research and forgiveness health benefits

Advocates of the theory that forgiveness enhances health report that, following therapeutic forgiveness sessions where the wounded are guided towards a more positive outlook and perception of the offender, the health benefits are significant. Among the identified health outcomes were:

- Improved cardiovascular function,
- Relief of depression,
- Reduced chronic pain, and
- A boost in the quality of life for those suffering illnesses.

A national survey published in the *Journal of Adult Development* in 2001[9] revealed some interesting statistics. It found that only 52% of Americans reported that they had forgiven others for hurtful acts. Although the findings in regard to health benefits did not reveal anything striking among younger respondents who practised forgiveness, the impact was clearly noted in those of middle age. The data from the survey demonstrated that respondents of 45 years and older who forgave others reported better overall mental and physical health than those who did not practise forgiveness.

Everett Worthington, a leading researcher on the links between forgiveness and health, and professor of psychology at Commonwealth Virginia University, has undertaken numerous case studies in this field. In the process his study subjects are taken through the principles of forgiveness and the resulting physiological effects are measured.

Worthington strongly believes in both the positive principles of forgiveness and its power to influence health and wellness in those who embrace it. He reports that the foundation on which his view of forgiveness is built is due firstly to his Christian upbringing. However, he is also clear about the value of scientific evidence and embraces positive research outcomes from studies that have rigorously tested the impact of forgiveness.

Among these was the evaluation of a carefully constructed process of 'how to' forgive. Worthington found that when the hurt individual was taught how to replace hostility and negative feelings with those of compassion, empathy or even love for the offender, and was able to come to this point by him/herself, it enabled him/her to temper or reverse the physiological stress of chronic anger and the associated emotional repercussions.

In 1996 Worthington's own ability to forgive was put to the test when his elderly mother was bludgeoned to death in her apartment by an intruder with a crowbar. A suspect was arrested and charged with her murder. Unfortunately, justice was never served. Although the suspect initially confessed to the crime, irregularities in the handling of evidence resulted in his being released. In spite of this, Worthington resolved not to let this heinous crime destroy his life. He stated that he had run the full course of shock, anger and grief, and within a month of his mother's death was ready to forgive.

How was he able to do this? Worthington states: 'I look back and I think, for me, what a mercy from God that I could spend eight years examining forgiveness before I had to deal with it. I had already thought through so many of these issues before I had to apply them.'[10]

Dr Tibbits on 'Forgive to Live'

One outstanding piece of research in the area of forgiveness comes from the Florida hospital where Dr Dick Tibbits led a scientific study known as 'Forgive to Live'. The actual research is titled *'Hypertension Reduction Through Forgiveness Training: How Forgiveness Can Save Your Life'*.[11] The data provided scientific proof of the link between undertaking forgiveness training and a resulting significant reduction in blood pressure. It also demonstrated how the process of forgiveness works to effect changes in areas of emotional well-being, like decreased anger and subsequent health improvement.

Dr Dick Tibbits has produced some powerful resources on forgiveness in which he outlines the processes involved in forgiveness, the benefits we achieve as a result and what happens when we choose not to forgive. In his book *'Forgive to Live – How Forgiveness Can Save Your Life'*, the book sleeve carries this overview: 'Every one of us has a "grievance story" – a hurtful event perpetrated by someone who mattered in our lives. And for most of us, that hurt simply will not go away. Enter forgiveness. . . . Unfortunately, while most of us have been taught we should forgive, we've never been shown *how* or *why* to forgive.'

His series of resources (books, workbooks, CDs and devotionals) outline three key phases of forgiveness:

Phase 1: How I handle the memories of painful things said and done to me in the past.

The Healing Power of Forgiveness

Phase 2: How I overcome the negative emotions I feel right now.

Phase 3: How I free myself from a hurtful past to achieve my desired future.

Dr Tibbits further breaks down the dimensions of forgiveness into three key aspects: the relational (conflict between two individuals), the spiritual (accepting God's forgiveness and extending it to others), and the personal (learning to forgive yourself).

Having undertaken the 'Forgive to Live' course myself, I found it to be a practical, scientific and biblical approach which was immensely powerful. I have since used its principles both in my life and in teaching forgiveness to others through workshops and other training presentations.

The holistic impact of forgiveness

The head chaplain at the world-renowned Mayo Clinic defines forgiveness as a 'decision to let go of resentment and thoughts of revenge', and to untie yourself from thoughts and feelings about the offence committed against you'.[12]

Researchers at the same clinic have undertaken studies which demonstrate that holding on to grudges can lead to health problems.[13] Ongoing research suggests that nursing a grudge can place the same physical strains on the body – for example, tense muscles, elevated blood pressure, increased sweating – as those caused by a major stressful event.[14] Additionally, these research outcomes continue to suggest that psychological repercussions such as resentment, anger, guilt and anxiety were more common in people who were unable to forgive.

Physical benefits of forgiveness

Among the health benefits associated with the letting go of hurts and resentments, researchers found forgiveness to be positively associated with improvement in five measures of health: physical symptoms; medications used; sleep quality; fatigue and somatic complaints.[15]

Reduction in stress response: Research from the Mayo Clinic suggests a lowering of the stress response in individuals who readily forgive.[16] This was evident in reduced muscle tension, fewer complaints about nervous symptoms, and fewer palpitations and panic attacks.

The Healing Power of Forgiveness

Improved heart health: Studies have found that forgiveness is good for the heart. One study from the *Journal of Behavioral Medicine*[17] found forgiveness to be associated with lower heart rate and blood pressure.

The pain impact: Studies from the Mayo Clinic and the Duke University Medical Centre on individuals with chronic pain demonstrated a reduction in pain symptoms in those who were more forgiving. One study at the Duke University Medical Centre highlighted people with chronic back pain reporting less pain and anxiety when they focused on converting anger to compassion.[18]

Dr Douglas Russell, a Veterans Administration cardiologist, stated that eruptions of anger at others have been shown to increase the risk of heart arrhythmia, heart attacks and high blood pressure. He conducted a study in 2003[19] which found that the coronary function of patients who had suffered a heart attack improved after a ten-hour course in forgiveness. Additionally, it was found that when anger is turned inwards, bottled up and directed at oneself, the impact was even more negative. It appeared that lack of forgiveness and the inability to express that anger in a wholesome way resulted in the individual becoming toxic, with chronic health conditions. This appeared to be more damaging to physical and mental well-being than when the anger was expressed outwardly.

Emotional benefits of forgiveness

Stanford researcher, Frederic Luskin, has studied the effects of forgiveness and defines it as '. . . the moment-to-moment experience of peace and understanding that occurs when an injured party's suffering is reduced by the process of transforming a grievance they have held against an offending party'.[20]

Although more research is needed to formally evaluate the

health benefits of forgiveness, a number of small studies[21] have indicated some potential health benefits that may be conferred by forgiveness:

- Improved conflict resolution
- Better recovery from trauma
- Decreased anger and fewer negative thoughts
- Decreased anxiety
- Decreased depression and grief
- Decreased vulnerability to substance abuse.

Spiritual benefits of forgiveness

'For if you forgive men their trespasses, your heavenly Father will also forgive you. But if you do not forgive men their trespasses, neither will your Father forgive your trespasses.' Matthew 6:14, 15.

Whenever we pray the Lord's prayer, we hold ourselves to account to forgive others. When we repeat Matthew 6:12, which says, 'And forgive us our debts, As we forgive our debtors', we are asking God to offer us forgiveness in the same manner that we extend forgiveness to others. So then, if we are unforgiving to others we are literally telling God to treat us in the same way.

Forgiveness is related to love. When we forgive an individual we extend love to that person, just as Christ extends love to us in His forgiveness of our sins. *Forgiveness* promotes inner peace, deepens our spiritual experience and makes us more Christlike.

The Gospel (meaning Jesus' Good News) tells us to love those who hate us. (See Matthew 5:43-48.) In our society we don't know how to truly forgive. Instead we seek to get even. Or we say, 'I forgive that person, but I won't forget.' How many of us can truly say that we have let go of the past memories, hurts and pains without them really affecting our spiritual life, our characters, our emotions, our decisions, our relationships and our actions?

The Healing Power of Forgiveness

When we open our hearts to the truth of God's Word it will lead us to all good works: *'bearing with one another, and forgiving one another, if anyone has a complaint against another; even as Christ forgave you, so you also must do.'* Colossians 3:13.

God gives us the prescription for forgiveness in Ephesians 4:31, 32 (NLT), which says: *'Get rid of all bitterness, rage, anger, harsh words, and slander, as well as all types of evil behavior. Instead, be kind to each other, tenderhearted, forgiving one another, just as God through Christ has forgiven you.'*

Forgiveness from the heart is not based on conditions. It is given whether the offender asks for it or not. As painful as it is, we are to offer forgiveness even when we think the person does not deserve it. God forgives unconditionally and He has removed our sins as far from us as the east is from the west (Psalm 103:12).

Fact:

- Identifying current feelings about past events gives you a starting point from which to assess where you are in the process of forgiveness.
- Negative emotions must be addressed and explored. This assists in the journey towards forgiveness.
- Holding on to hurts solidifies an unforgiving attitude.
- The act of forgiveness engenders health benefits for mind, body and spirit.

Action:

Manage your feelings by doing the following exercises:
- Recall an incident that caused you pain or bring to mind the person who hurt you. Take note of the feelings the memory evokes. This is a good indicator of whether you are still upset or angry about the incident or the hurt that the individual caused you.

- Ask God to give you the desire to forgive and help to heal the hurt of that experience.
- Try to convert the emotional build-up and time you expend in constantly rehearsing how unfair a challenging incident was by diverting your energy into exploring ways of letting the hurt go. This may require professional help.
- Repeat Matthew 6:12 every time the memory of that negative incident, or that person who hurt you, comes to mind.
- Tell yourself every day that forgiveness is possible.
- Seek special prayer and/or counselling if you are struggling in this area.

To forgive yourself is a tonic to your heart and mind; to forgive others is a weight-relieving experience.

- *Letting go of grudges* is health-enhancing as well as energising. According to a study in the journal *Psychological Science*,[22] nursing a grudge stimulates the mind and body to react as if under chronic stress. This increases the heart rate and blood pressure, which can lead to an impaired immune system and exhaustion over time. However, practising empathy and forgiveness following a wrong done to you makes you feel more in control, which helps to regulate the body's stress response.

The Healing Power of Forgiveness

When forgiveness hurts

On 31 December 2007 an article appeared in the *Los Angeles Times* captioned 'Forgive and be well?' Journalist Melissa Healy, author of the article, examined the evidence on the impact of forgiveness. She commences by saying, 'The act of pardoning can boost health of body and mind, studies show. But some say the forgiveness movement goes too far.' In the article she balances the scientific reports on the positive health impact of forgiveness with the view of sceptics that if forgiveness is forced or indeed false it may even do damage to the individual.

She presents arguments from both sides. Advocates of the theory that forgiveness enhances health report that, following therapeutic forgiveness sessions where the wounded are guided towards a more positive outlook and perception of the offender, the health benefits are significant. Among the identified health outcomes are improved cardiovascular function, relief of depression, reduced chronic pain and a boost in the quality of life for those suffering illnesses.

On the other side of the argument is research that suggests forgiveness can be damaging if the victim feels pressurised to forgive. While many scientists would conclude that forgiveness is beneficial and endorse the studies indicating physical and mental gains, there are concerns from practitioners in the mental health field for patients who are considered vulnerable.

They fear that forcing traumatised patients to forgive prematurely, or when they are feeling most vulnerable, can prove counterproductive and even harmful.

Jeanne Safer, a psychoanalyst from New York and author of *Must We Forgive?* reasons that for many patients forgiveness is another hurdle to overcome.[23] It is in fact like a double blow. Firstly they are deeply wounded by an individual; then, they are made to feel guilty that they have negative thoughts about that individual. She states: 'I'm not against forgiveness; I'm against compulsory forgiveness with no choice. And I'm against "forgiveness lite", which keeps you from feeling the intensity of the experience, from deeply grappling with what's been done to you.'

Echoing these concerns is Linda Davis, the executive director of Survivors of Incest Anonymous.[24] She has found, in working with victims of incest, that many of them have internalised the suffering by blaming themselves. Davis adds that compounding the self-blame that victims experience is the fear that forgiveness will involve reconciliation with an abuser whom they never wish to see again, and the pressure to forgive can be extremely stressful to the point of seeming impossible. In such cases the forgiveness process becomes a sensitive and often protracted one. A timely and patient approach of supporting the individual going through the process is key to them achieving forgiveness at a pace that they can cope with. Being judgemental and rushing the process (putting pressure on them to move on and forgive) will not help them heal and certainly not result in a well-thought-through decision to forgive.

Reflection:

- It seems, then, that forgiveness is something that needs to be learnt. Additionally, for some individuals, particularly those who have been severely traumatised by a past hurt, it may require intensive support and a sensitive approach to help them deal with the trauma and memory of the event.

The Healing Power of Forgiveness

- Acknowledging the individual's pain and 'staying' with them through the healing process will enable them to be supported and strengthened to face the prospect of forgiveness.
- Professional counselling support, ongoing prayer and spiritual guidance may be necessary interventions to further assist the individual struggling to forgive.

Applying the biblical model

What is the biblical directive on forgiveness?
Let's look first at how we are taught to forgive, and then at the consequences when we do not forgive.

When someone wrongs you:

- Go directly to the individual and make a personal and private appeal to sort out the issue. Matthew 18:15 (KJV) states, 'Moreover if thy brother shall trespass against thee, go and tell him his fault between thee and him alone: if he shall hear thee, thou hast gained thy brother.'

What happens if he or she responds negatively?

- If the offender does not wish to engage with you or refuses to make peace, try to get a mutually respected mediator to assist you. Matthew 18:16 (KJV) says, 'But if he will not hear thee, then take with thee one or two more, that in the mouth of two or three witnesses every word may be established.'

What should you do if the offender refuses to listen to you or others acting on your behalf?

- If the individual refuses to listen to either you or the witnesses you bring to them, then the matter is escalated to another level and is brought before the church. Matthew 18:17 advises, 'And if he refuses to hear them, tell it to the church. . . .'

The Healing Power of Forgiveness

What happens if the offender refuses to acknowledge the church's advice on the matter?

- If the offender will not listen to the church, then it is evidence that he or she is not acting as a Christian should. In this case the individual becomes like an 'unbeliever' and is therefore in need of your prayers and positive witness in the same way that we would treat someone who is not a Christian. Matthew 18:17 continues, '. . . But if he refuses even to hear the church, let him be to you like a heathen and a tax collector.' However, such offenders still need our forgiveness.

What happens when we forgive someone who has hurt us?

- 'For if you forgive men their trespasses, your heavenly Father will also forgive you.' Matthew 6:14.

What happens when we do not forgive someone who has hurt us?

- 'But if you do not forgive men their trespasses, neither will your Father forgive your trespasses.' Matthew 6:15.

What should you do if you offend someone?

When we have wronged others or caused pain or injury to them, the Bible is clear about how we should behave.

- Ask for God's forgiveness. This is illustrated in the Lord's Prayer, where we are taught to pray: 'And forgive us our debts, as we forgive our debtors' (Matthew 6:12, KJV).

When we sin against others we need to do something about it. 'Debts' may be defined as sins of omission, which include duties or obligations that we have left unfulfilled. 'Trespasses' may be defined as sins of commission, where we commit acts which God has told us not to do.

- Go to the person you have wronged, honestly confess your wrong, and, as far as possible, make restitution for any injury or loss you have caused.

The biblical directive in Matthew 5:23, 24 is clear: 'Therefore if you bring your gift to the altar, and there remember that your brother has something against you, leave your gift there before the altar, and go your way. First be reconciled to your brother, and then come and offer your gift.' This passage of Scripture tells us that, before we worship God, we need to put things right with those who are offended because of us (irrespective of whose fault it really is). Worship in this context comes after the act of forgiveness.

Reconciliation – is it always possible?

If an individual is willing to forgive you for a wrong that you have done, then reconciliation is possible. The same happens if they wrong you and come to seek your forgiveness and you offer it. However, if you seek reconciliation from someone who has hurt you and they refuse to apologise or admit their wrong, then reconciliation is not possible. The same is true if you have wronged an individual who refuses to forgive you. If reconciliation is attempted but forgiveness is not forthcoming, then you have done what you can do and God will accept that. The apostle Paul recognised that it takes two persons to reconcile a difference and bring resolution to an existing conflict. In Romans 12:18 he states, 'If it is possible, as much as depends on you, live peaceably with all men.' When you have done your part, leave the rest to God.

How should we behave towards those who hurt us?

Sometimes the thought of consistently trying to do what is right to someone who does not have your best interest at heart can feel draining and upsetting, and even stretch your faith.

The Healing Power of Forgiveness

How should you respond when the situation remains unresolved?

Resist the desire for revenge and reject the right to retaliate

- Proverbs 20:22: *'Don't take it upon yourself to repay a wrong; leave that to the Lord.'* (The Clear Word.) *'Don't say, "I'll pay you back for the wrong you did." Wait for the LORD, and he will make things right.'* (NCV.)

Release the hostility that you feel towards the ones who inflicted pain, injury or loss on you

- Matthew 5:44, 45: *'But what I'm telling you is to carry out acts of love for your enemy, too. Ask for a blessing on them when they curse you. These actions show that you are the children of God. . . .'* (The Clear Word.) *'But I say to you, love your enemies. Pray for those who hurt you. If you do this, you will be true children of your Father in heaven. . . .'* (NCV.)

Don't become resentful when God blesses them too

- Matthew 5:45: *'. . . Look at what your heavenly Father does! He makes the sun to shine on everyone, good and evil alike. Also, He waters the crops for those who do right and for those who don't.'* (The Clear Word.) *'He causes the sun to rise on good people and on evil people, and he sends rain to those who do right and to those who do wrong!'* (NCV.)

Remember that you need forgiveness from God too

- Matthew 6:14, 15: *'When you pray this way, remember that the answer to your prayer is conditional. If you forgive others, your Father will forgive you. But as long as you have an unforgiving attitude, it would not be right for your heavenly Father to forgive you.'* (The Clear Word, 2004.) *'Yes, if you forgive others for their sins, your Father in heaven will also forgive you for your sins. But if you don't forgive others, your Father in heaven will not forgive your sins.'* (NCV.)

Pray continually for the one who has hurt you

- Mark 11:25: *'And whenever you stand praying, if you have anything against anyone, forgive him, that your Father in heaven may also forgive you your trespasses.'*

Make a deliberate decision to repay good for the evil that has been done to you

- Luke 6:35: *'But love your enemies, do good, and lend, hoping for nothing in return; and your reward will be great, and you will be sons of the Most High. For He is kind to the unthankful and evil.'*

Extend mercy to others as God extends mercy towards you

- Luke 6:36: *'Therefore be merciful, just as your Father also is merciful.'*

Don't pass sentence on others

- Luke 6:37: *'Judge not, and you shall not be judged. Condemn not, and you shall not be condemned. Forgive, and you will be forgiven.'*

Action:

- Take some time to go over the segments of this chapter and consider your response in relation to each of the statements.
- Prayerfully consider the points highlighted and, as you review each one, commit to God any aspect you are struggling with.

The Healing Power of Forgiveness

- Use the statements in bold and their associated Scriptures as a discussion point in your church.
- You may wish to pray through each statement and Scripture with a prayer partner or use them as a prayer focus in your prayer groups.

Lessons from the olive

Olives may not be on your list of culinary delights but they are a favourite food of mine. Black olives, green olives, marinated olives, stuffed olives – whatever the variety or recipe, I just love them! To some olives are an acquired taste; others avoid them altogether. While some individuals may not like the taste of olives, their health benefits have been researched for several decades. Scientific research has produced data which attests to the healing properties of the olive, in particular its leaf.

Current research on the olive leaf extract has identified that the bitter substance in the olive leaf, called oleuropein, is responsible for its therapeutic properties. Classified as an antioxidant, the reported benefits of olive leaf extracts range from promoting increased energy and healthy blood pressure to treating infections and supporting the cardiovascular and immune system.[25]

Just think of it: something that tastes as bitter as the olive leaf, which we would want to discard, is embraced as a remedy and used medicinally in order to bring healing. As with the bitterness of the olive leaf, life with its traumatic experiences can sometimes be like a bitter pill to swallow – one we would rather discard.

Life experiences that have caused us pain and embittered our lives can be used to heal our pain. The stories in this book illustrate that fact. They show that the challenging life experiences people encounter, which could be described as a

The Healing Power of Forgiveness

'bitter pill to swallow' because of the emotional pain they cause, can have a positive outcome. With the passage of time and after having reflected on these experiences, many have been able to conclude that, in spite of it all, the learning and growth that ensued have made them better, stronger people.

There are people, however, who will tell you that at some point in their lives they have been hurt so deeply that forgiveness was hard to contemplate at the time. It is not uncommon to hear such people say that they vow they 'will never forgive them for what they did'. Sadly, some of these embittered individuals have kept those grudges going to their deathbeds without resolving the issues that caused them pain, or making peace with those who upset them.

Medical science (as stated in the chapter titled *'Research and Forgiveness'*) can now demonstrate the harmful effects of choosing not to forgive and holding on to resentments. Among the emerging evidence researchers have presented is data suggesting that over a lifetime the failure to forgive could raise a person's risk for heart disease, mental illness and other debilitating conditions. Some studies have suggested that forgiveness actually improves health. Evaluation of this data highlights the correlation between learning good lifestyle health habits and learning how to build emotional resilience. It is suggested that, just as we can successfully learn how to apply proper diet and exercise to enhance our well-being, so we can learn how to forgive in a way that preserves health and prevents disease.

There is, however, another notable element to the olive, particularly its branch. The olive branch also symbolises peace. Historically, the phrase 'to extend the olive branch' is a reference to extending a peace offering as a sign that one wants to end an existing conflict. It is this concept that comes to mind when I think of forgiveness. In essence you are extracting healing from a bitter experience by using forgiveness as the prescription. Reflecting on the olive branch as a symbol of peace and healing, the same can be said of forgiveness when it is extended to others. Forgiveness can bring peace to conflict situations so that both the recipient and the one offering forgiveness can experience the healing and reconciliation.

The Healing Power of Forgiveness

Moving from bitter to better

'As I walked out the door toward the gate that would lead to my freedom, I knew if I didn't leave my bitterness and hatred behind, I'd still be in prison.' Nelson Mandela

Following the death of Nelson Mandela, US President, Barack Obama, gave a moving tribute to the life of Mandela and the tools he used to overcome a prison sentence that could have embittered him but enriched him instead. In his speech he stated:

'. . . His journey from a prisoner to a president embodied the promise that human beings – and countries – can change for the better. His commitment to transfer power and reconcile with those who jailed him set an example that all humanity should aspire to, whether in the lives of nations or our own personal lives. And the fact that he did it all with grace and good humour, and an ability to acknowledge his own imperfections, only makes the man that much more remarkable. . . .'

Then again on 10 December 2013, at Nelson Mandela's funeral, while recounting the impact of Mandela's life, Obama said:

'It took a man like Madiba to free not just the prisoner, but the jailor as well; to show that you must trust others so that they may trust you; to teach that reconciliation is not a matter of ignoring a cruel past, but a means of confronting it with inclusion, *generosity and truth. He changed laws, but also hearts.'*

As Obama concluded his speech he made reference to a poem that Mandela often quoted during his incarceration. A poem that gave him the hope for a better future – something to which he could aspire while facing the reality of prison. His closing remarks sum up a life that sought to overcome the negatives of the present to embrace the possibilities of a brighter tomorrow.

'After this great liberator is laid to rest; when we have returned to our cities and villages, and rejoined our daily routines, let us search then for his strength – for his largeness of spirit – somewhere inside ourselves. And when the night grows dark, when injustice weighs heavy on our hearts, or our best-laid plans seem beyond our reach – think of Madiba, and the words that brought him comfort within the four walls of a cell:

> *"It matters not how strait the gate,*
> *How charged with punishments the scroll,*
> *I am the master of my fate:*
> *I am the captain of my soul."*

What a great soul it was. We will miss him deeply.'

What a positive impact one life can make when one chooses to live out forgiveness instead of living with and perpetuating hatred. Indeed, we are the masters of our fate as we choose to deal with our hurts; and we are the captains of our souls as we choose how to handle our emotions. Mandela turned his pain to positive action and the world will remember him.

So how does this apply to us in our everyday lives?

Dealing with painful life events can be a challenging experience. It is easy to see how immense suffering, injustice and abuse can make an individual become bitter. Pain can certainly bring out the worst in people, but it can also shape them into better people. Forgiveness can forge the link between the past and the present, the present and the future. It can be the catalyst that propels an individual forward; the key ingredient that, when added to the life of the suffering individual, can beam the light of hope into the darkness of despair. The bitter can indeed become palatable.

Anne Gallagher[26] is someone who is acutely aware of the bittersweet experience of the forgiveness journey, having lost her brother to the violence in Northern Ireland. She says this about forgiveness:

'Forgiveness isn't something that's talked about with reconciliation, but it's needed to bring closure to the pain and suffering experienced in Northern Ireland. You can't contemplate hope unless you address despair. To heal the wounds of Northern Ireland I believe you have to see humanity in the face of the enemy. But forgiveness is a journey. Today you can forgive and tomorrow you can feel pain all over again. I'm not a religious person, but for me forgiveness is about grace. To be able to forgive someone who has hurt you is a moment of grace.'

What powerful words. I find the reference to grace deeply moving because it reminds me of the way God treats us, in spite of who we are and what we have done. He extends His unconditional love towards us in offering us His forgiveness.

How did Anne come to have the strength of character to forgive in this way? She saw it demonstrated. Continuing her story, she states:

'My mother is my driving force. She has such a respect for every single soul – even for the policemen and soldiers who raided our house and caused her so much pain.'

Anne's story is a remarkable one. As a former nurse from the Royal Victoria Hospital (RVH) in Belfast, she nursed many victims, including policemen and soldiers who were wounded during bullet and bomb attacks on 'both sides of the sectarian divide'.

Yet in the face of all this human tragedy it was her resolve to live for a better tomorrow that kept her going in spite of setbacks. 'Her brother Dominic, a former IRA member, became leader of the Irish National Liberation Army (INLA).' At that time, he was 'the most wanted man in Ireland' and was eventually captured and imprisoned. However, 'After his release from prison he was shot dead by unknown gunmen.'

Having 'experienced the pain of having close relatives imprisoned and killed' in the early days of 'The Troubles', Anne has a lot to be hurt about. Some would even say that if she were to have become bitter it would have been justifiable. This, however, did not happen.

As a result of the devastating effect of the 'war' in Ireland, Anne founded an organisation called Seeds of Hope, which encourages individuals to 'tell their story' of 'The Troubles' through writing, art, music, drama and sport. Her work has been emulated in several European countries and in the USA in schools, communities and prisons. What positive and far-reaching impact can ensue because one person chose to forgive.

Reflection:

- Anne stated that one reason why she learned forgiveness is because her mother demonstrated it.
- We may be able to point to only a few people in life who can exemplify such depth of forgiveness in the face of personal tragedy. However, Jesus is our true example, because when He hung on the cruel cross on Golgotha's hill, He forgot about Himself and His pain and thought only of others and the need to forgive them for what they were doing. In the midst of the unimaginable physical, emotional and spiritual pain and torture He endured, He was able to say of His enemies, those who were responsible for His death, 'Father, forgive them; for they know not what they do.' (Luke 23:34, KJV.)

The Healing Power of Forgiveness

- If you think you are having a hard time forgiving others for what they have done to you, just think of what Jesus endured in order to save us; yet He was able to forgive.
- It was His forgiveness that turned the 'bitterness' of the cross into the beauty and 'sweetness' of Calvary. That secured a better future for each of us.
- Don't get bitter – get better.

Action:

- Each time you are tempted to be unforgiving – think of Calvary.

Letting go of the baggage

Unforgiveness is like heavy baggage that weighs us down. When we hold on to painful memories and refuse to let them go, it reinforces their weight, making them a bigger burden. We also tend to focus on the wrong that others do to us, while ignoring the fact that we too are committing a wrong by choosing not to forgive. Essentially, because we see those who cause us pain as the perpetrators and initiators of our suffering, we focus on that one fact, and heap judgement and condemnation upon them.

'If you judge people, you have no time to love them.' This was one of the famous statements that Mother Teresa made as she ministered on the streets of Calcutta. Instead of passing judgement on why people were in the positions that she found them in (most of them destitute and living on the streets) whether it was due to their own life choices or not, Mother Teresa realised they needed help. Therefore she chose to respond to their present circumstances rather than their past history and the issues that had brought them to that point.

I have found that the issue of forgiveness becomes more challenging when we gauge our efforts to forgive someone who has wronged us by trying to decipher whether they deserve it or not. In so doing we tend to weigh up the person's history or their present behaviour to see whether they have 'earned' the right to be offered our forgiveness. It is clear to me that when we place 'judgement' above 'love' it is harder to forgive.

In the previous chapter entitled: 'Moving from bitter to

better', I shared the story of Anne Gallagher from Northern Ireland, who overcame personal tragedy to set up an organisation called 'Seeds of Hope' to help others learn to forgive.

Continuing her story Anne states:

'I grew up in County Derry in a very happy family, one of four sisters and seven brothers. I'd just started nursing when my father and three of my brothers were interned without trial. It was this that got my other brothers involved in The Troubles. In the hospital Intensive Care Unit, I would nurse victims from all sides. Seeing them lying there, naked and attached to life support machines, I didn't see a uniform, I just saw their hearts, their pain. The conflict was everywhere: out on the streets, in people's houses, at the end of your bed during night raids, when you'd wake up to find uniformed men in your room. My brother Dominic was murdered in front of his young son, who had previously, with his other young brother, seen his mother shot as she bathed them. I absolutely loved my brothers. I didn't judge them at all.

'With the Seeds of Hope project, we encourage people not to judge others. We listen to people's stories, but we don't judge them. There's healing in that. The idea is that when you hear my story and I hear your story, it becomes our story, and seeds of hope are sown.'[27]

Edward Herbert said, 'He who cannot forgive others breaks the bridge over which he must pass'.[28] When we refuse to forgive it embitters our lives, especially when we wait for opportunities to 'pay back' the individual who has hurt us. Jean Paul Richter said, 'Humanity is never so beautiful as when praying for forgiveness, or else when forgiving another.'[29]

The greatest demonstration of forgiveness was seen in the act of redemption when God took human hatred in its vilest form – the death of His Son – and used it to demonstrate divine love at Calvary when Jesus gave up His life for mankind.

The story is told of a general who attended a service where

the preacher John Wesley was speaking. He sat and listened to Wesley deliver a sermon on forgiveness. Afterwards, in conversation with the preacher, he reportedly stated: 'I can never forgive' – to which Wesley replied, 'Then, sir, I hope you never sin.'[30]

Reflection:

- Recall again that incident that caused you pain or bring to mind someone who hurt you. How did you respond in that situation?
- Are you still finding forgiveness a challenge?
- What part did you play in the process with regard to any conflict that ensued?
- Can you think of a way that you could make amends if you were a contributor to the conflict?

Action:

- If the individual who has caused you hurt is no longer alive, pray that God will give you the strength to release the negative memories you hold of how they hurt you.
- Next, ask God to give you the willingness to extend the 'olive branch' of reconciliation where possible.

The Healing Power of Forgiveness

Forgiveness – a step-by-step journey

> 'The gem cannot be polished without friction, nor man perfected without trials.' – Chinese proverb

Most people, when recounting their forgiveness journey, will tell you that while the end goal of freedom from the bitterness of unforgiveness appeared desirable, they first had to deal with the pain that was blocking their progress. In my discussions with people who have attended my *'Forgiveness As Healing'* workshops, many of them have talked about the transformation that forgiveness has brought to their lives. However, it was not just the act of forgiving that made them feel better – it was also the end of the pain of their unforgiveness and the lessons that it had taught them. The challenges along the way – confronting the pain of the past; dealing with the struggles of the present; admitting their fears for the future; and overcoming the hurdles at each stage of the journey – all this contributed to the end result. It was all part of the success of arriving at the forgiveness destination.

For each individual the story varies in some way but, almost without exception, each one mentioned this common denominator – the fact that the journey took time.

Forgiveness should not be rushed, as the journey is different for everyone. Indeed, more harm can be done by forcing forgiveness to the point that the injured party begins to feel like the perpetrator. Unless they are allowed to complete their forgiveness journeys without undue pressure they may feel branded as failures and their self-loathing can be intensified, with damaging results. Evidently, the forgiveness journey that allows the individual to come to the choice of forgiveness themselves, in a timely way, results in the most lasting benefits.

Clinicians are becoming more outspoken on the impact that forgiveness has on clients with deep emotional scars. They advise caution in the way we assist hurt individuals to achieve healing. Clinical intervention with these individuals, whom clinicians classify as 'vulnerable', has revealed that sometimes those who appear to forgive others more quickly (often with pressure from a relative or clergy member) do so because they blame themselves for the bad things that have happened to them.

Psychoanalyst Jeanne Safer identifies what she calls 'fake forgiveness',[31] where people forgive too quickly because they don't want to acknowledge the feelings they have of shame and anger, or sometimes because they simply feel unworthy of being treated better. Therefore they justify the treatment from the perpetrator, and forgiveness then appears an easier option. Safer sees this as harmful, as it allows these 'victims' to continue blaming themselves and 'owning' the wrong done to them.

Other clinical studies done by researchers such as Lydia Temoshok, a clinical and social psychologist at the University of Maryland's Institute of Human Virology, have revealed similar results.[32] Temoshok reports that, having worked with and studied several individuals who have had traumatic experiences, she found that chronic self-blamers tend to be overly willing to forgive others who have wronged them without really addressing their own hurt.

This was particularly evident in her study of patients infected with HIV. Classifying these patients as 'Type Cs', Temoshok

The Healing Power of Forgiveness

reveals their distinct reaction. 'They are not the hard-charging, angry Type As who are given to heart disease, or the easy-rolling, deal-with-it Type Bs who tend to enjoy better health, but the ones who deny problems, suppress strong feelings and tend to stay in stressful situations longer, putting their health at greater long-term risk.'

In the same way that a physical wound takes time to heal and cannot be rushed, we should take the same care with emotional trauma and give people time to heal from their emotional wounds. It is clear, then, that a sensitive and timely approach to forgiveness is necessary to effect healing that is sound, and to prevent adverse effects in the long term.

Some time ago, while preparing material for a presentation on emotional well-being, I found myself studying Psalm 30:5. It reads: 'Weeping may endure for a night, But joy comes in the morning.' I have always found this a very comforting and hopeful Scripture. It acknowledges that even though we experience pain in the present, our dark night of tears will give rise to hope, and joy will eventually emerge with the dawn of a new day. However, as I examined the passage more closely, I realised that we often use this passage enthusiastically to 'help' or hurry people over their hurt, when what they really need at that time is for you to sit with them, endure with them, waiting with them through the 'night' of their experience until the light dawns for them. Our intentions may be well meant as we try to offer support, but we also need to be aware of the individual's emotional journey.

People are generally uncomfortable with pain. Whenever we see someone upset or in tears we instinctively want to comfort them or try to cheer them up in order for them to 'feel better'. This is even more pronounced when someone experiences a significant hurt. In an effort to try and bring things back to normal, we try to hurry them through their healing.

'Weeping may *endure* for a night. . . .' If that is the case, let us learn how to endure with others in their moments of pain. If we stand with people in their pain and wait with them for their healing to happen, we enhance their healing process because it occurs naturally, and not through pressure or force. When we try to push people quickly past the pain to the more comfortable position of forgiveness and resolution, they lose the growth that is necessary during that time of challenge which will, in fact, strengthen them for whatever lies ahead. We also halt their potential to deal with greater challenges which may come in the future.

The story of the butterfly is a poignant one and demonstrates the concept of struggle bringing growth. I have heard it told many times on different occasions with slight variations. However, the message is always the same: struggle brings development.

The story is told about a man who saw a butterfly struggling to get out of its chrysalis. He watched it struggle, then stop for a while, then recommence the struggle, only to stop again for a while – and so the process went on. The man began feeling sorry for the butterfly, thinking how difficult it was for it to get out. Uncomfortable at seeing it struggle, he decided to make things a little easier by assisting it. He got a pair of scissors, thinking that if he cut the cocoon just a little, it would enable the butterfly to get out quicker and with less effort. This he did.

Having made the cut, the butterfly crawled out easily. He noted, however, that it did not look the same as other butterflies, but had a fat body with withered wings. The man decided to wait and watch to see if the butterfly would spread its wings, but the wings did not open up. Sadly, the man realised what had happened. In order for the butterfly to develop its wings it needed to endure the struggle at the chrysalis stage. It was this struggle which would have forced fluid from its body

The Healing Power of Forgiveness

into its wings to enable them to unfold. Without the struggle of getting out of the chrysalis, the butterfly had not been able to pump enough fluid from its body into its wings. The struggle therefore served an essential purpose: that of developing the butterfly to fulfil its purpose, to fly and exhibit its true beauty. The struggle was essentially what made the butterfly beautiful.

Reflection:
- When we rush people past their struggles in order to 'help' them, we stall their development. This hinders their potential to become the best they could be.
- If you find yourself quick to offer therapy to others, ask yourself whether it could be because you are uncomfortable with their pain.
- Development takes time. Forgiveness is a journey. Let people get to that destination in their own time.
- Don't dictate when and how people should forgive, as their speed of healing and the needs they have may be different from yours.
- Try not to compare your experience of forgiveness and healing with theirs, as we are all individuals. Even if the circumstances of their pain are similar to yours, remember that each individual will perceive, experience and respond to that situation from a different perspective.
- You best assist the forgiveness journey of others when you stand with them to give your support, but do not take over.

Action:
- When helping an individual through the painful process of forgiveness, ask God to help you to be patient, gentle and wise in your approach, both in words and in actions.
- If you are finding your own forgiveness journey challenging, then be gentle with yourself and remember

that Jesus took all our pain, suffering and guilt on Himself so that we would not have to remain in our seemingly hopeless condition, but through Him receive the abundant life and the strength to face every challenge.

The Healing Power of Forgiveness

Forgiveness that brings healing

Over the years I have read many accounts of forgiveness, and heard testimonials and stories of individuals who have overcome great difficulties and emerged as powerful examples of what it means to forgive. What follows next is one account of victim and perpetrator that has been deeply etched in my mind. I have been privileged to speak with the author and have been given permission to share the interview she undertook with the victim and her perpetrator.

Journalist Jina Moore wrote a deeply touching piece titled *'No Small Mercy'*, published in the *Walrus* magazine,[33] which is the transcript of the account of a Rwandan woman, Alice Mukarurinda (Tutsi), who narrowly escaped death at the hands of Rwandan Emmanuel Ndayisaba (Hutu) in the genocide. Jina states: *'Fifteen years after Rwandan Hutu massacred hundreds of thousands of their Tutsi countrymen, one survivor and the man who cut off her hand tell the horrible truth about the genocide and explain how, even with so much suffering between them, they eventually made peace.'*

Here is part of Alice's story:

'. . . After the plane crashed, the road out of Nyamata was blocked by the soldiers and Interahamwe. *We couldn't escape, so my husband and I and our nine-month-old daughter, Fanny, fled to the church. It was packed with people. My mother was inside; she told me to stay outside so the baby could breathe.*

'There was a big mass of people outside the church, too. My husband was preaching. Some men asked him to go and fight the

Interahamwe *with them, but he said he would fight them with his Bible. Everybody who could teach in the name of God was doing it. We preached, we sang. We prayed any way we could think of.*

'*On April 11, the* Interahamwe *attacked the church. They killed my mother and two sisters. My husband and I ran with our daughter to a bean field. That night, we slept in a school. For seven days, we hid among bean plants and banana trees during the day and slept in the school after the* Interahamwe *left.*

'*When the* Interahamwe *set fire to the fields, we ran thirty kilometres to the swamps to hide in its grasses. My husband ran to one side, and I ran to the other. But the* Interahamwe *were not far behind, slinging their machetes back and forth through the reeds, trying to hit anything. This went on for ten days.*

'*I had Fanny on my knees, and my niece next to me, when a soldier finally found us. He looked at my baby and said, "She's beautiful. She must be the child of Fred Rwigema," who founded the RP. "Where is this baby's father? Did he run away?"*

' *"I don't know," I lied. "I left him two or three days ago. He might not even be alive."*

Then he took all my clothes.

' *"You know," he said, "your government has abandoned you. I can kill you." He had a machete in one hand and a club in the other.*

'*I told him, "Do what you came here to do."*

'*He shook his head. "My arms are not made for spilling the blood of people." Then he left.*

'*Later, a whole group of them came back. They took my baby from me. They threw her in the air, and they cut her in two, down the middle. I fell down, crying. They started hacking me with machetes. They drove a spear through my shoulder and struck my head with a club studded with nails. They left when they thought I was dead. I heard my niece cry, "This one, now she is dead, too!"*

'*An old woman appeared, a Hutu neighbour who had run with*

The Healing Power of Forgiveness

us because her husband was Tutsi. She saw and heard everything that happened to me, and she took her head wrap and tried to reattach my hand with it. Then she took more fabric from around her waist, and we wrapped up my baby. I was too injured to move, so she left with my baby. From there, I can't remember anything. I died for five days.

'I woke up in the swamp, with lots of dead bodies around me. They smelled, and dogs were eating them. My husband found me there. He told me they had thrown him into a well; he'd had so much water in his body that they had to pump it out of him.

'Then he showed me our baby. "We're going to have to bury her," he said. But there was no place to bury her properly. We could only cover her up. I still can't bury her, because I never want to go back there.

'While I was unconscious, the Inkotanyi had taken control of the district. Now they were asking the able-bodied to come out of the swamps and join them. Still very weak, I stayed there for two more weeks, until my husband could get me to a hospital. It was mid-May when he carried me out of the swamp on a door.

'When I left the hospital two months later, we moved into a house shared between ten families. We eventually got a house of our own with help from the government, and some of my husband's relatives who had returned to Rwanda stayed with us. They didn't understand what happened; they didn't live through it. They told my husband I was handicapped and would not be any good to him anymore. They asked him, "Will you wash your kids' clothes? Will you be the one to raise them? Let us find you a new wife." My husband looked at me like I was useless. But he told them, "What happened to her could just as easily have happened to me."

'I didn't expect to ever meet Emmanuel. I didn't even remember his face. My neighbours pushed me to join the association because I stayed at home too much. I lived in my thoughts about the

*genocide and about the problems I still faced. I knew this group
was for people who survived and people who were getting out of
prison for genocide. I wondered how we could accept these people
into our communities again.'*

Alice describes the moment she came face to face with the
man who almost killed her. He had come to the fields where she
was working. She continues the story:

*'. . . He asked if he could talk to me. "I have something to tell
you," he said. "I have a big problem." He kept repeating this. "I
have a big problem, I have a big problem." After twenty minutes,
he fell on his knees and asked me to forgive him.*

*' "Why?" I asked him. "We are friends. What do I have to forgive
you for?" He just kept saying, "Forgive me, forgive me," and I kept
asking why. Finally, he said, "I'm the one who cut you."*

*' "What did you say?" I asked him. He repeated, "I'm the one
who cut you." I asked him to tell me where and when. He did; his
story was all true. So I left him there, on his knees, and I ran for
miles.*

*'For Emmanuel, it was easy, because he was ready to ask. He
had prepared his heart, and he had prepared a way to do it. I was
in shock. I didn't say if I had forgiven him or not. I couldn't really
answer either way. So I left him in a place that was not
comfortable for him either.*

*'After I left, a woman found me. She took my hand and led me
home. She told my family what happened. My husband said,
"This is your fault. Why did you join an association with killers?"*

*'I spent one week thinking about it all the time. People
sometimes asked who had hacked me, and I couldn't answer them.
But I knew I wasn't born like this! I needed to know who did this
to me, because I was judging everyone around me. The people
living across from us – they took a lot of our things, so maybe they
were the ones? I wanted to forgive and live normally with people
again.*

The Healing Power of Forgiveness

'Still, I had a hard time when Emmanuel revealed himself to me. It took me back to 1994. My husband reminded me, "You promised God that if you found out who did this to you, you would forgive him. Why are you hesitating?" So when I went back to work, I was the first one to greet him. I told him, "I forgive you. God will forgive you."

Emmanuel Ndayisaba, who killed many people in the Rwandan genocide and who was responsible for Alice's horrific injury, tells his side of the story.

' "Alice is the last person I cut. I cut off her hand and made a scar on her face. I thought I killed her. And then I stopped killing. Something had begun to bother me.

'I was a singer in an Adventist church, and there's one song that says when our time comes, all the riches we've accumulated are not going to follow us, and that the person who spends his life pursuing them will only attract Satan. Partly, I was afraid of Satan. I was also fed up. I saw the faces of all of the people I killed before me. I remembered I had sung in front of them in church. I thought, "How come I killed the same people I was singing for?"

'It was time to stop. Still, I had already taken their things, and I decided those things would stay in my house.

'After the Inkotanyi *ended the genocide in Rwanda, they formed a new government. In 1996, I went to a district court to turn myself in. I started to tell the judge what I did, but I was talking so fast, like a crazy person, that he asked if I was sane. I said, "I can't cope with it anymore. I just want to be forgiven." Then he asked, "Who are you asking for forgiveness from? You killed almost everyone." I answered, "Since there is nobody left, I am asking forgiveness from the government, because I killed its people."*

'A month later, they sent me to prison. I went with my father. We were packed like beans, one under another. Of course, people were beaten. The police told the guards that I had confessed and that

they should be nice to me. I was allowed to work outside, cooking and cleaning for the policemen. My father, who did not co-operate with the courts, died from sickness in prison. I was there for seven years, until the amnesty. Paul Kagame, the president of Rwanda, said that anyone who had confessed could be freed.

'Still, if somebody killed your family and then got out of prison, you would be unhappy. At the same time, if you had killed you would not be comfortable facing your victims. That's why four ordinary people in Nyamata started an organisation called Ukuri Kuganza Guharanira Ubumwe N'ubwiyunge *(May Truth Bring Unity and Reconciliation). I joined in 2005. We wanted to have a place to talk and to plan how we would build a future together, so we borrowed some land, and together – hundreds of us – we raised crops and animals and built houses.*

'After prison, before going home, we went to Ingando, *re-education camps where the government teaches unity and reconciliation. Some people who'd had a chance to ask forgiveness from survivors found they could be traumatised by it, acting like someone who's gone crazy. At* Ingando, *they told us that when we asked for forgiveness we should find a way to do it so that they could be held by their friends if they needed them.*

'Even though I didn't know if Alice would accept, after I said "Forgive me", everything was easier for me, even eating. For the first time in a long time, I felt the food go into my stomach. Before, I had no appetite, even when my stomach was empty. It was like a huge stone was lifted off me, and my neck could stretch and my head could rise up, because the stone was not there anymore.

'Now we are close friends. When I need something and she has it, she will give it to me. If I have something more than she has, I will give it to her. We can sit down and share food.

'Even today, I see the faces of the people I killed. They pass before my eyes without speaking to me. I think they are silent because the dead can't forgive. Can you imagine? You killed

someone you don't even know, and he passes before your eyes, and he will never talk to you.'

Reflection:

- Forgiveness has no limits
- Reconciliation requires forgiveness, but forgiveness does not demand reconciliation.
- What does forgiveness look like? It looks like love.

Action:

- Take a moment to reflect on your thoughts as you read the above story and write down what you were feeling.
- Put yourself in the place of Alice and Emmanuel and imagine what the forgiveness journey was like for each of them.

What's your story?

> 'Resentment is like taking poison and waiting
> for it to kill the enemy.' – Nelson Mandela

Following his release after twenty-seven years in prison, the late Nelson Mandela has been quoted numerous times on how he used the power of forgiveness to fuel hope for the future so he could live without resentment about the past.

His was indeed a story of pain, and for many his time in prison appears as 'wasted years' during which he was robbed of freedom. Yet that story of pain and injustice did not define him in a negative way. In fact, he used that very experience of pain to make himself a better person, free himself of resentment towards his captors and move forwards with his life. He went on to lead his country and seek out opportunities to perpetuate the message of forgiveness and its powerful impact.

We all have a story to tell about pain. Most people can tell of an incident where they have been hurt in some way, or they can relate an experience of someone causing them significant harm or loss. However, when they are asked about how they presently feel about what has happened to them, it is not unusual to hear that bitterness has set in. They show residual resentment and anger towards the individual who hurt them and often vow never to speak to that person again or forgive them for what they did.

The Healing Power of Forgiveness

Far from being a healthy stance to take, scientific evidence exists to show that when we hold on to resentment and choose not to forgive, it can cause significant harm to our well-being and results in poor health. Much research into psychosomatic disorders has shown the strong correlation between our thoughts and attitudes and our physical illnesses and poor health.[34]

Dr Tibbits, author of the 'Forgive to Live' programme, has treated countless patients who suffer from significantly poor health. In several cases, where medication and other lifestyle changes proved ineffective, deeper analysis of the individuals' emotional well-being indicated that resentment and anger were at the heart of their emotional unrest and physical illness. However, his scientific research, entitled *'Hypertension Reduction Through Forgiveness Training'*, clearly demonstrated that individuals suffering with high blood pressure and unresolved emotional issues that made them resentful and angry had their blood pressure return to normal when taken through the 'Forgive to Live' programme.

Equally important is the way we recall what has happened to us. The way we recount the painful episodes, the story we tell others about what we have gone through, can play a significant part in our healing and our journey towards forgiveness. One aspect of Dr Tibbits' forgiveness programme talks of how our healing can be impeded by the way we tell our story. It is what he refers to as 'the birth of the grievance story'.[35] This is when the person who has been wronged recounts the woeful tale of what happened to them. In doing so they attach a specific interpretation to that event and come to a conclusion of why it happened, irrespective of whether that conclusion can be verified or not. As the individual repeats the story over and over to themselves these negative aspects of what occurred are amplified and begin to nurse the grievance. This is reinforced every time they tell the story to others.

Dr Tibbits emphasises what he calls the 'grievance story toxicity', where the impact of retelling the experience in a negative manner begins to have an effect on the individual. A key part of helping to overcome our grievance, and the story we tell ourselves and others, is to see the incident from a different perspective and then retell it in a different way – one which allows us to release the hurt and not hold on to it.

The longer we hold on to grievances and retell our story in a negative way, the more resentment takes over.

The story of two prisoners of war standing at a memorial wall illustrates this. One said to the other, 'Have you forgiven your captors?'

'Never,' the other responded.

'Then I guess they still have you in prison,' the first speaker replied.

Reflection:

- When we fail to release those who hurt us we continue to be held prisoner to past memories. Don't let resentment keep you in 'prison'.
- When we repeatedly rehearse the wrong done to us it breeds negative self-talk. This impacts the way we view ourselves and others, which is generally in a negative way.
- What is your story?
- How are you telling it?

Action:

- Think of the last time you told your 'grievance story' to someone. Can you remember how you told it and the emotions you attached to it? If so, rewrite what you said (still stating the facts) but this time include the fact that you are asking God to help you put the pain associated with the memory behind you.

- When you next share your story of what happened to you, reword the account by leaving out every little detail of the emotion you attached to that event. This is not to deny the pain you felt at the time but it is a step towards preventing the further embedding of the feeling of hurt and resentment and resurrecting the harshness of the painful emotions over again.

Forgiveness in practice

It was Alexander Pope who said this: 'To err is human; to forgive, divine.'[36] Many have embraced those words, somehow thinking that forgiveness is almost out of the reach of our human capacity. However, many others have found that forgiveness is not as unattainable as it may seem, or even a near impossibility in some extreme circumstances. I saw forgiveness modelled one afternoon when a visiting congregation came to present a programme at the church I was attending at that time.

The programme was a fusion of testimonies and songs by the visiting choir. The songs warmed our hearts but it was the testimonies that left a lasting deep impression on me as to what forgiveness really was. You see, in the choir were Hutus and Tutsis singing side by side. Then unfolded the account of the 1994 Rwandan genocide, in which it is estimated that between 800,000 and 1 million people lost their lives – an alarming statistic. But as shocking as those figures sounded, more sobering was the realisation that among both victims and perpetrators were Christians.

One by one, each choir member shared his or her recollection of their forgiveness journey, describing how either they or their family members were caught up in the massacres that took place. The details were gruesome and not for the faint-hearted, but they revealed that Christians killed fellow Christians. The account was painful to hear, and so was the enormity of what they needed to forgive. I could also sense the great weight of the unforgiveness which had oppressed them

The Healing Power of Forgiveness

for years before they were able to encounter the liberating power of forgiveness.

Along the very difficult and painful journey to forgiveness some developed emotional, mental and physical illnesses due to the burden of that unforgiveness. Some indicated that they were still undergoing medical and psychological treatment and support as a result of their trauma.

For some the challenge had been not to recount the story with bitterness to their children (who would often ask them about the massacres), so as not to encourage seeds of hatred to germinate and discourage any chance that revenge might be perpetuated from generation to generation. Others told of how they soon realised that the way they recalled the memories of the atrocities impacted their journey of forgiveness. From experience they found that the more they talked about it in negative terms, the more hurtful the memories became and the more they felt a sense of outrage. This would then fuel more anger, making it harder to put the trauma behind them or to even contemplate forgiveness.

For one lady the journey to forgiveness was a tortuous one. She described the day she came close to losing her life. She recalled that as she was running from her attackers, one of them caught up with her and, using a machete, struck her with great force across her body. She described the lasting scar that extended from the top of one shoulder all the way across her body down to her hip. Her challenge was that every time she made a decision to forgive and tried to put the trauma behind her, seeing the scar would bring back terrible memories of the event. She was forced to come face to face with them every time she took a bath or shower – there was the permanent reminder of what had happened to her.

How do you move on in life when everywhere you turn your past is there; your pain is visible; and your worst nightmare is a living reality? How do you move forward under such circumstances? Is forgiveness possible under such conditions?

That afternoon the answer was modelled for us as each of them told us how God had helped them to forgive – to the extent that some Hutus went on to marry Tutsis and vice versa. There were even choir members who had married someone despite knowing that he had killed members of their family.

One widow told of how she had married the man who had killed her parents. Another even married one of the men who had killed her husband! Can you imagine that? Others who lost all their siblings married into the family of the people responsible for their murders.

Can you grasp the enormity of what it took to embrace an individual who had committed such an atrocity against those you loved? And in the light of such dark tragedy and intentional evil, just think of how challenging it must have been to make the transition from what could have been lasting hatred to forgiveness. Yet by comparison, we can pass our brother and sister and not speak to them because of some trivial issue that we have magnified beyond reason. I sat in awe and listened with deep conviction to each forgiveness story, resolving that in spite of my own life hurts I had nothing to complain about. In fact, I just needed to be more willing to forgive.

I was particularly interested in the testimony of the lady who had the permanent scars left by her attacker. At first she hated to hear the word 'forgiveness' because it seemed to mean that what her attackers did to her was not that bad, or that it did not really matter too much, just as long as her life was spared. Yet here she was struggling to move on from the nightmare she encountered, but reliving the trauma every time she looked at herself in the mirror. She was also suffering significant pain from the scar tissue, which caused her ongoing health problems. Additionally, the emotional scarring from the

The Healing Power of Forgiveness

frequent flashbacks she encountered inhibited her ability to sleep soundly and negatively affected her moods, leaving her feeling sad most of the time.

She recalled that the final step in her forgiveness journey was one day during her devotional time. She had begun to contemplate the life of Jesus and the negative encounters He had with people. Among these the one that gripped her most was Him hanging on the cross in agony, but pausing to pray for His abusers: 'Father, forgive them . . .' It was the rest of that prayer, 'for they do not know what they do', however, that really brought her to the realisation of the extent to which Jesus went to 'release' His cruel perpetrators. That despite his inhuman torture and lasting scars he could still forgive those who had caused them! She realised at that moment that forgiveness was possible.

It did not happen overnight, but little by little, as each day unfolded, she recalled the crucifixion and prayed: 'Father, help me to forgive like you forgave.' With this repetitive and committed action she came to the point where she could give her testimony without feeling hatred or the desire to see her attackers punished.

Reflection:
- Forgiveness is not an easy process, but with God's help and a focus on Jesus' example it becomes possible.
- You may not feel ready to forgive, but by using Jesus' example of 'stating' His forgiveness you prevent the root of bitterness from taking hold in your heart. It may be a while before you really feel the spirit of true forgiveness, but saying the words 'I forgive' reinforces your intention to let go of bitterness.
- Remember, the evidence of forgiveness becomes apparent when you can recall the incident and everything done to

you but no longer feel the resentment, bitterness and desire for revenge against whoever caused it.

Action:

- Take time to connect with someone you know who has been able to forgive a terrible wrong done to them and see what you can learn from their journey.
- Spend some time reflecting on the crucifixion, and, as you do so, think of the person you find it hard to forgive, then repeat the words of Jesus: 'Father, forgive them, for they do not know what they do.'
- Take the next step by voicing the words, 'Father, I too forgive . . .' and include the name of the person or persons who have hurt you as you ask God to help you forgive them.

The Healing Power of Forgiveness

The forgiveness test

> 'Forgive us the wrongs we have done, as we forgive the wrongs that others have done to us.' Matthew 6:12, GNB

For as long as I can remember I have asked myself what this passage of Scripture means in practical terms. Every time I read it or recite it in my prayers, it causes me to stop and assess what I am actually saying or asking of God. My query is particularly with reference to the phrase, '. . . and forgive us our debts *as we* forgive'. Does it mean that while I am in the process of asking God to forgive me, I need to extend the same forgiveness to others? Is it that if I am to expect forgiveness from God I should also expect to forgive others?

In life it is inevitable that others will trespass against us, just as in our human weakness we will trespass against them and God. In asking for forgiveness from God for our sins against Him, the breach in our relationship is repaired and our relationship is restored. We need also to couple that with a request for forgiveness from those we have wronged. By asking forgiveness from God we are reconciled to Him. In the same way we need to seek forgiveness from others for the wrongs we have done to them in order to bring healing and, where possible, reconciliation.

Another interpretation of 'forgive us . . . *as we forgive* those . . .' could be referring to the *manner* in which we approach forgiveness. Is it actually saying that I am asking God to forgive me in the same way that I forgive others? That is, if I forgive others graciously, am I asking God to forgive me graciously, but if I forgive others grudgingly, am I asking God to treat me like that as well?

Can you imagine God forgiving us the way that we forgive others? I know that I have not done too well in this area in the past. Generally, if I have had to confront an individual who kept offending me, I would do so grudgingly: 'Well I forgive you this time, but don't do it again!' Or I would be tempted to find an occasion to bring up the incident some time later, either to remind the person of their wrong and the hurt it caused, or as a warning to make sure they don't repeat the offence!

Just imagine what it would be like for our emotional and spiritual well-being if God forgave us, but then kept bringing up our transgressions from time to time; or if His forgiveness were to come with a threat or caution. Under such circumstances we would not feel the release from our burden of guilt and enjoy the freedom and liberty in Christ that we now enjoy and which He intended for us to have.

What does the following text mean to you? '. . . forgive us . . . *as* we forgive those . . .'

There are three observations I have made over the years, in line with this passage of Scripture.

1. Accepting God's forgiveness is key to our deliverance and healing.

2. We can expect forgiveness from God, for 1 John 1:9 tells us: '*If we confess our sins, He is faithful and just to forgive us our sins and to cleanse us from all unrighteousness.*' He gives His forgiveness freely to us; we have only to ask for it.

3. Most people who cannot accept that God has forgiven them have trouble forgiving others. If you cannot accept that God has forgiven you, then you will not have

experienced the joy, release and healing that forgiveness brings – and it will be hard for you to extend to others what you have not experienced yourself.

Let's examine the word 'trespass'. Most of us have seen 'no trespassing' signs, especially outside private property and other places of restricted access. To trespass would be to break the law, and there are likely to be consequences as a result. You could be arrested, prosecuted and fined, or even be exposed to physical danger.

When we sin against God we are guilty of trespassing against Him – of breaking His divine law, that spiritual code of conduct He has laid out for us. We deserve to be punished for this, but God sent us Jesus to bear the consequences at Calvary, dying in our place so that we might be set free. What an awesome God!

He pardoned us, offering us grace that we do not deserve. Why can't we extend the same pardon and grace to each other?

Many of us have been wounded in our homes, our churches, our places of work and our communities. Yet in spite of this hurt, we can act graciously, like God, and forgive.

So what are the challenges that you face? What are the trials that buffet you from day to day? What are the stumbling blocks on the track of your life, impeding your forgiveness journey?

No matter what they may be you can face them successfully if you realise that God is there alongside you.

Some time ago while speaking with some colleagues about the impact of unforgiveness, the challenges on the forgiveness journey became very evident. Among those they mentioned were:

- Emotional strain – mostly related to trying to work out what their issues were
- Judging oneself – feelings of guilt or self-blame about the perpetrators' actions towards them and the possibility that

they (as perceived victims) are partly to blame for their own pain
- Feeling 'rushed' by others to forgive
- Having to prove to themselves and others that they were 'moving on' from the hurt
- People judging them on the way they have forgiven in the past
- Negative spiritual impact as they wondered why God had allowed them to be hurt in that way
- Feelings of being punished by God because of the injury that was inflicted on them
- Doubts as to whether, in our human capacity, we can forgive in the same way Jesus forgave those who persecuted Him
- Guilty feelings about the way they forgive – for example, thinking they have forgiven someone and then experiencing residual negative feelings about that person.

Reflection:
- How easy is it to forgive, particularly when the injury is a significant or repeated one?
- Think of a time when someone hurt you really badly. Were you able to forgive them readily?
- If so, what did it feel like to forgive and really mean it?

Action:
- If you are having a hard time forgiving someone for the hurt they have caused you, think of a time when you know you have really hurt the heart of God and ask Him to forgive you the wrong you did or the dishonour you brought to His name. Conclude your time of reflection by thanking God for His forgiveness.
- Next, think of someone whom you have hurt and ask God

to give you the grace to approach them and ask for forgiveness.

- Now bring to mind the individual or individuals who have caused you pain and ask God to give you the desire to forgive them. Keep presenting this request to God each time you pray until the unforgiving spirit you have nurtured is no longer there.

Practical pointers for achieving forgiveness

If the thought of having to forgive more than once seems daunting, or if you find forgiveness a challenge, then the following may prove helpful in getting you started. These steps were formulated following a research project.[37]

1. Know exactly how you feel about what happened and be able to articulate what about the situation is not OK. Then, tell a trusted couple of people about your experience.

2. Make a commitment to yourself to do what you have to do to feel better. Forgiveness is for you and not for anyone else.

3. Forgiveness does not necessarily mean reconciliation with the person that hurt you, or the condoning of their action. What you should be after is to find peace. Forgiveness can be defined as the peace and understanding that come from blaming that which has hurt you less, taking the life experience less personally, and changing your grievance story.

4. Recognise that your primary distress is coming from the hurt feelings, thoughts and physical upset you are suffering now, not what offended you or hurt you two minutes – or ten years – ago.

5. At the moment you feel upset, practise a simple stress management technique to soothe your body's 'flight or fight' response.

6. Give up expecting things from other people that they do not choose to give you. Recognise the 'unenforceable rules'

The Healing Power of Forgiveness

you may have for your health, or how you or other people must behave. Then remind yourself that you can hope for health, love, peace and prosperity, but that you will have to work hard to achieve them.

7. Put your energy into looking for another way to get your positive goals met than through the experience that has hurt you. Instead of mentally replaying your hurt, seek out new ways to get what you want.

8. Remember that a life well lived is the best revenge. Instead of focusing on your wounded feelings, and thereby giving the person who caused you pain power over you, learn to look for the love, beauty and kindness around you. Forgiveness is about personal power.

9. Amend your grievance story to remind you of the heroic choice to forgive.

The 70 X 7 principle

Peter asked Jesus a probing question: 'Lord, how often shall my brother sin against me, and I forgive him? Up to seven times?' Jesus said to him, 'I do not say to you, up to seven times, but up to seventy times seven.' Matthew 18:21, 22.

Jewish tradition in biblical times limited forgiveness to three times for someone who had wronged you. It's clear that Peter thought that by offering his forgiveness to a brother who had sinned against him as many as seven times, he was being magnanimous. This willingness to forgive seven times was much more generous than Jewish tradition, and thus surpassed the righteousness of Pharisees and teachers of the law (Matthew 5:20).

God forgives all sins, and He forgives regardless of the number or extent of the transgressions. There should be no limits to forgiveness. Jesus demonstrated this on the cross when he extended grace to the thief crucified beside Him. Although we do not advocate that individuals wait until the point of death to repent, we see in this biblical account that it is never too late to turn to Christ and ask for mercy.

When I read this Bible verse for the very first time I was amazed at the scale of forgiveness to which I was to aspire. Seventy times seven? That's 490 times! Who would stay around long enough for someone to hurt them that many times? Come on!

I call this passage of Scripture the '70 x 7 principle', and I generally thought that it was just saying that we ought to forgive

The Healing Power of Forgiveness

as many times as an individual offends us. This did not necessarily mean counting up all the 'misdemeanours' of those who offend us until they reached the 490 limit, after which we could slam shut the door of forgiveness on them! However, I was still concerned about the issue of boundaries. How do you forgive in a way that does not allow the offender to keep on hurting or abusing you? What about self-respect? No one likes to be stepped on repeatedly. Surely it is folly to make yourself vulnerable to repeated abuse. However, this is not necessarily what this Bible passage is saying.

The 70 x 7 principle is also saying that every time I remember that I was hurt, whenever I recall the wrong done to me or the offender comes to mind, instead of seeing it as an opportunity to feel aggrieved, angry or bitter – in that moment of remembrance – I must choose to forgive. I ought to forgive as many times as the offence or offender comes to mind, just as I ought to forgive them as many times as they cause me hurt.

Reflection:
- Is there something you are currently angry or hurt about?
- Is it a recent incident or one that happened some time ago?
- We are directed in Scripture to exercise forgiveness towards those who trespass against us and cause us pain, no matter how many times they offend us.
- What are the boundaries you put in place to prevent yourself being vulnerable and open to being hurt repeatedly?
- While the directive to forgive as many times as we have been hurt by others is one that we are required to follow and therefore accept, we also need to be wise in terms of where the boundaries of acceptance and safety become blurred and we become vulnerable to abuse.

- Keeping ourselves safe is important so that we do not become an easy target for individuals who may seek to harm us.

Action:

- Think of a current or past challenge that you have with forgiveness. Try to decipher whether the issue of repeatedly forgiving that individual is having a negative impact on you or poses a degree of risk to you in some way.
- Separating yourself from the individual or reducing the contact time may be necessary until the situation is resolved.
- If there is a risk that the individual might try to push boundaries, therefore making you vulnerable, seeking intervention in the form of mediation, counselling or other professional support may well become necessary.

The Healing Power of Forgiveness

Being at peace with yourself

There has been much talk about forgiving others who have caused you hurt. However, how do you forgive yourself when you have made choices that were unwise, or taken decisions which have turned around to harm you in some way? How do you introduce the 'olive branch' into your own internal conflict about who you are and why you made poor decisions in the past? Is it easier to be at peace with yourself by forgiving yourself for these mistakes than having to extend the olive branch to someone else who has wronged you? How do you handle things when you are at fault?

Psychologist Toussaint states: 'The human mind is sometimes an instrument of misery. When you've done wrong to others and regret it, it bubbles up again and again, . . . there's no escaping the perpetrator.'[38]

Toussaint further states: 'Sometimes people hurt us, and we move on, and it might fade. . . .' However, building on previous work to better define forgiveness and the experience people go through on the forgiveness journey, Toussaint reports his surprise at learning that individuals holding on to self-blame don't fare so well. He says, 'Forgiveness of self holds the more powerful punch, . . . the effects are dramatic.'

Toussaint undertook an interesting study which showed gender differences in relation to forgiveness and empathy.[39] During a study of male subjects and their forgiveness response, Toussaint discovered a negative outcome for emotional well-being in men who did not readily forgive themselves. It was found that they were seven times more likely to be diagnosed with clinical depression than men who are able to forgive themselves. Equally revealing was the data for female respondents. The study showed that highly self-forgiving women were three times less likely to have the symptoms of clinical depression than their female counterparts who were prone to regret and self-blame.

It is a well-researched fact that clinical depression is a risk factor for other illnesses. Therefore the link between forgiveness challenges and depression is a cause for concern. Furthermore, it was found from the data that individuals who were more forgiving of themselves got more sleep and were in better overall health.

Other compelling evidence for the negative impact of self-blame on our health has been seen in a study of war veterans by Julie Hall and Frank Fincham.[40] It highlighted the emotional strain and psychological health effects in combat veterans who returned home without being able to forgive themselves for actions they took, or did not take, during battle. Similar outcomes have been found by researchers examining self-blame and forgiveness challenges in patients with cancer and HIV/AIDS, and the victims of abuse and incest who in some way blame themselves for their fate.

Reflection:

- Think of a situation where your actions caused hurt, harm or conflict to develop. Release the pain and guilt of that memory to God and ask for His forgiveness.
- If you are still blaming yourself for something that you have done wrong, realise that just as God is able to forgive you for whatever you did wrong, you can forgive yourself too. If you are finding this difficult then a good Christian counsellor may be able to assist you in the process.

The Healing Power of Forgiveness

- Resources such as Dr Tibbits' *Forgive to Live* series are excellent tools to help you learn how to forgive yourself (*www.ForgiveToLive.net*).

Action:
- If the individual you hurt is still alive and you have not yet asked for their forgiveness or been reconciled with them, pray for the strength and wisdom to approach them humbly and ask for their forgiveness. This will help to assist you on your journey of self-forgiveness.
- If the individual is no longer alive or you are unable to physically reach him or her, then the previous points will still be of help.

Let the healing begin

'Hope is the companion of power, and mother of success; for whoso hopes, strongly has within him the gift of miracles.' Samuel Smiles

With healing comes hope.

Hope and forgiveness are linked. When you forgive, you give yourself a better future as you free yourself of any bitterness that could blight the prospects of a brighter tomorrow. When I think of the words 'hope', 'healing' and 'forgiveness', I often think of Nelson Mandela and his long walk to freedom, which taught the world a lesson on forgiveness, reconciliation and the dignity in which we can endure injustice, yet still stand up to what we know is right.

The forgiveness journey may be a long and arduous one; but it is a road that eventually leads to freedom. It's a freedom from bitterness, from endless emotional strain, from spiritual stagnation and from social handicaps that can shipwreck human relationships.

Perhaps you can see your forgiveness journey the way Mandela viewed his journey for freedom. He wrote:

I have walked that long road to freedom. I have tried not to falter; I have made missteps along the way. But I have discovered the secret that after climbing a great hill, one only finds that there are many more hills to climb. I have taken a moment here to rest, to

The Healing Power of Forgiveness

steal a view of the glorious vista that surrounds me, to look back on the distance I have come. But I can only rest for a moment, for with freedom come responsibilities, and I dare not linger, for my long walk is not ended.[41]

On 5 December 2013 Nelson Mandela's long walk to freedom ended. He died, but his legacy on the power of forgiveness lives on. Following release from a twenty-seven-year prison sentence at the hand of the unjust apartheid system, he was able to extend the olive branch of forgiveness, hope and healing which brought some level of reconciliation to a divided nation. In spite of what he suffered, he modelled forgiveness with great integrity and tenacity of spirit.

At the beginning of this book, I commenced by sharing an incident of how hurt I was by a harsh email sent to me. I told you of the struggle I had to let the matter drop and release the individual from being locked into my present experience and thereby spoiling my joy. I ended by telling you that I had a choice to hold on to that hurt or to release it. I chose to release it and, even as I write this chapter, I can now smile when I remember the state I got myself into in my response to that event. Now, whenever the individual's name is mentioned or my mind recalls the incident, I no longer feel the associated hurt in the way I did before. I have released the hold that individual had on my mind by choosing to forgive. I tell myself not to hold on to the hurt or anger I felt when the injury occurred.

I have also, of course, prayed for a forgiving spirit (a forgiving attitude) towards that person. This has allowed my subconscious to come under the power of the Holy Spirit, so that even when I *think* I have totally forgiven that person and human nature rises up causing me to remember or replay the issue, God's help is there because I have asked for it. Furthermore, maintaining a prayerful mode enables God to give me the strength to go on forgiving that person if they offend me again.

Some time ago, as I was talking to God about forgiveness, I decided to write a list of all the people who had caused me pain over the years. Then one by one I prayed over each name, asking God to release those individuals from my mind. I asked Him to bless them and their families and to help me to think positive thoughts towards them every time they came to mind. It was an amazing experience. I began to feel a sense of release and realised how light one can feel when the burden of an unforgiving spirit is lifted from our hearts. It also helped to heal my 'wounded' spirit. I have found forgiveness to be a prescription for healing.

Missionary Elisabeth Elliot was one woman who not only knew the power of forgiveness but took a step further by accepting an assignment that would put the knowledge of this truth to the test. She was called by God to minister to the very tribe that had earlier murdered her husband. For many of us, that would have been too much to ask.

She could have questioned whether God really meant her to travel there in person. Perhaps He just meant her to minister to them long-distance – by praying for them, or sending them encouraging letters and useful parcels full of daily provisions. She could have felt that she was being asked to take on an assignment much too weighty and painful to bear. However, after a brief time of hesitation, she came to know the practical meaning of the word 'acceptance'.

Imagine coming to terms with something of that magnitude – the murder of your spouse – and feeling that through forgiveness that chapter of your life was closed, only to find that a door reopens and brings you face to face with that painful past once more. How do you move on into a hopeful future when the ugly past reappears like this? Sadly, it often does, just when we think we are over it. As hard as it may seem, how we handle that situation will test the endurance of our forgiveness.

Realising that she couldn't run from God's will for the rest of her life, Elisabeth could have taken up the assignment grudgingly, resentful that she had been called to bear such a burden. However, in taking up the challenge she was to become a shining example of how to accept and activate the will of God in our lives. She eventually took up her assignment with confidence, knowing that God would enable her to fulfil it. Sometimes on the journey to forgiveness, God may ask of you something bigger than you expect. But if He asks you to do so, it is because He knows that you can do it in His strength.

Because of this experience Elisabeth was able to pen the following words: 'Only in acceptance lies peace . . . not in resignation.' And what a difference between the two. In the journey to forgiveness, do you just grudgingly resign yourself to the fact that you have to forgive, or do you willingly accept it as a directive from God to enhance your life and the lives of others?

The author, Creath Davis, writing on the impact of acceptance and resignation, makes these poignant statements:

'Resignation is surrender to fate. Acceptance is surrender to God. Resignation lies down quietly in an empty universe. Acceptance rises up to meet the God who fills that universe with purpose and destiny. Resignation says, "I can't." Acceptance says, "God can." Resignation paralyses the life process. Acceptance releases the process for its greatest creativity. Resignation says, "It's all over for me." Acceptance asks, "Now that I'm here, what's next, Lord?" Resignation says, "What a waste." Acceptance says, "In what redemptive way will you use this mess, Lord?" Resignation says, "I'm alone." Acceptance says, "I belong to you, O God."[42]

Living the life of goodness is a sure way of developing a forgiving spirit.

It was probably John Wesley who said this: "Do all the good

you can, by all the means you can, in all the ways you can, at all the times you can, to all the people you can, as long as you can.'

Reflection:

- Do you want to live the 'good life'? Then recognise that forgiveness is at the heart of abundant living.
- Accepting that forgiveness is a way of life for the Christian will sweeten your walk with God and others. We live in an imperfect world with imperfect people. Hurt is therefore an inevitable part of life and we need to ask God to give us the grace to respond gracefully when we are confronted with it.
- Although pain is inevitable and we can't always avoid it, bitterness, misery and a vengeful spirit are optional, because we have the power to choose how to respond to life's hurts.

Action:

- Ask God to give you a spirit that is willing to accept His directive to forgive.
- If you have just resigned yourself to the fact that there is nothing else to do but to forgive, ask God to enable you to do it with joy, for in this way it releases you from any residual resentment that may be festering.
- Ask a prayer partner, 'accountability' buddy or friend to pray with you for help and support on your forgiveness journey.

The Healing Power of Forgiveness

A word to conclude

'Only the brave know how to forgive; it is the most refined and generous pitch of virtue human nature can arrive at.'
Laurence Sterne[43]

We all make mistakes and as such are all in need of forgiveness. God forgives unconditionally and He is our example. Belief impacts behaviour. If we are to emulate Christ we need both to *believe in Him* and to *behave like Him*. This includes the way we treat others when they hurt us.

As you have read the research outcomes of the scientific studies on forgiveness and contemplated the tips and suggested advice we discussed, I trust that you have been inspired to think again about the power of forgiveness and the healing that it can bring to your life and the lives of others.

You may have identified with the accounts of individuals who have been challenged to forgive in spite of the traumatic experiences they have encountered. As you recall your own bitter life experiences, think about how you can apply the soothing balm of forgiveness to each of them so that you can have healing, wholeness and hope.

As we have come to see, forgiveness is essentially the resignation of those feelings of resentment, anger or hurt for things done to us, and the resolve not to demand punishment or restitution for them. In addition, forgiveness is the gift that we give to others in response to God's forgiveness of our sins. God would not require us to forgive if it were impossible for us to do so. Forgiveness is a prescription God offers us when we falter on our Christian journey, feel the pain of guilt, confess our faults and ask Him for pardon. This brings healing to body, mind and spirit. We ought to extend that prescription to others.

We are reminded of this fact in Scripture: 'Be tolerant of one another. If someone has done you wrong, forgive him as the Lord forgave you the wrong you did to Him.' Colossians 3:13 (The Clear Word, 2004).

I love the following prayer, usually attributed to St Francis,[44] because it speaks of peace, forgiveness and hope, qualities we all need in order to live our daily lives. As you read the following words, think of how they can be applied to your life during your forgiveness journey.

> *'Lord, make me an instrument of your peace,*
> *Where there is hatred, let me sow love;*
> *Where there is discord, union;*
> *Where there is error, truth;*
> *Where there is injury, pardon;*
> *Where there is doubt, faith;*
> *Where there is despair, hope;*
> *Where there is darkness, light;*
> *Where there is sadness, joy.*
>
> *O Divine Master, grant that I may not so much seek*
> *To be consoled as to console;*
> *To be understood as to understand;*
> *To be loved as to love.*
>
> *For it is in giving that we receive;*
> *It is in pardoning that we are pardoned;*
> *And it is in dying that we are born to eternal life.'*

The Healing Power of Forgiveness

If you are struggling with painful memories of the past which are impacting your present and clouding your future, try praying this prayer every day and see if it makes a difference in your life. I am sure it will. It has done so for many others and you too can experience the same positive outcomes.

As I contemplate, again and again, this subject of forgiveness, I realise that we cannot control our past, but we can control the effect it has on our future. Perhaps you might like to try repeating the promise of Philippians 4:13 to yourself every day – *'I can do all things through Christ who strengthens me.'* This will assist you on your forgiveness journey when you feel that forgiveness is hard to put into practice. With God on your side, anything is possible. You can do it.

So here we are at the end of this little volume on forgiveness. As you reflect on the tools, tips and evidence from research chronicled in this book, my prayer is that God will guide your forgiveness journey; give you strength for the way and courage to face the days and years ahead. Embrace the possibilities that lie before you, knowing that there is a divine plan for your existence.

I pray that whatever your experience of forgiveness and wherever you may be on that journey currently, may you find the grace to forgive, and in so doing experience the healing and transformation that it brings. Know also that whatever has transpired in your past, whatever your present circumstances and whatever the future holds, God will grant you healing for yesterday, help for today and hope for tomorrow. Receive this assurance, believe God's promises for your life and apply the healing prescription of forgiveness to all your hurts. In so doing may you find that you are able to release the past with all its hurts, find freedom and peace in the present and embrace the future with a joy that you did not think possible.

References

[1] 'Forgive and be well?' Melissa Healy, *Los Angeles Times*, 31 December 2007.

[2] *Mere Christianity*, book 3: 'Christian Behaviour', chapter 7: 'Forgiveness'.

[3] 'The Last Word!' Lloyd H. Dunham, *www.dbcuuc.org/sermons/000423.html*

[4] *www.oxforddictionaries.com/definition/english/forgive*

[5] Tibbits, D. (2006), *Forgive to Live: How Forgiveness Can Save Your Life*, Florida Hospital, Thomas Nelson.

[6] Luskin, F., 2001, *Forgive for Good*, Harper: San Francisco.

[7] Witvliet, C. V. O. et al, 2008, 'Unresolved Injustice: An Investigation of Christian Commitment, Forgiveness, Negative Emotion and Cardiovascular Responses', *Journal of Christianity and Psychology*, 27, 110-119.

[8] Toussaint, L. and Webb, J. R. (2005), 'Theoretical and Empirical Connections Between Forgiveness, Mental Health and Well-being' in E. L. Worthington, Jr. (ed.), *Handbook of Forgiveness* (pp. 349-362), New York: Routledge.

[9] *Journal of Adult Development* 8 (4): 249-257, *hdl.handle.net/2027.42/44638* – Toussaint, Loren L.; Williams, David R; Musick, Marc A.; Everson, Susan A. (2001), 'Forgiveness and Health: Age Differences in a U. S. Probability Sample'.

[10] Worthington, E. L. (2005), 'More questions about forgiveness: Research agenda for 2005-2015' in E. L. Worthington, Sr. (ed.), *Handbook of Forgiveness* (pp. 557-575), New York: Routledge.

[11] Tibbits, D.; Piromalli, D.; Luskin, F. M.; Ellis, G. (2006), 'Hypertension reduction through forgiveness training.'

[12] Piderman, K., staff chaplain at Mayo Clinic, *MayoClinic.com*

[13] Piderman et al, Mayo Clinic staff, *MayoClinic.com*

14 Witvliet, C. V. O. et al, 2008, 'Unresolved Injustice: An Investigation of Christian Commitment, Forgiveness, Negative Emotion and Cardiovascular Responses', *Journal of Christianity and Psychology*, 27, 110-119.

15 *www.ncbi.nlm.nih.gov/pubmed/15957571*

16 Rochester, M., 2008, 'Learning to Forgive May Improve Wellbeing', Mayo Clinic, *Mayoclinic.com*

17 Witvliet, C. V., 'Forgiveness, Health and Wellbeing: A Review of Evidence for Emotional versus Decisional Forgiveness, Dispositional Forgiveness and Reduced Forgiveness', *Journal of Behavioral Medicine*, vol. 30, no. 4 (2007): 291-30.

18 Mary Hayes Grieco, 2011, 'Forgiveness and Health Research', Duke University Medical Centre.

19 Russell, D., 2003, cited in 'The Science of Forgiveness' by Melissa Healy – *Los Angeles Times*, 6 January, 2008.

20 Luskin, F., 2001, *Forgive for Good*, Harper: San Francisco.

21 Melissa Healy, 'Forgive and be well?' *Los Angeles Times*, 31 December 2007.

22 Witvliet et al, 2001, 'Granting Forgiveness or Harbouring Grudges: Implications for Emotion, Physiology and Health', *Psychological Science*, vol. 12, no. 2.

23 Jeanne Safer, New York psychoanalyst and author of *Must We Forgive?* cited in 'The Science of Forgiveness' by Melissa Healy – *Los Angeles Times*, 6 January, 2008.

24 Linda Davis, executive director of Survivors of Incest Anonymous, cited in *The Seattle Times*, Wednesday, 13 February, 2008.

25 *Phytochemistry* vol. 31, no. 4, 1992.

26 Anne Gallagher, 2011, *The Forgiveness Project*.

27 Ibid.

28 *The Autobiography of Edward, Lord Herbert of Cherbury*, revised edition (London: Routledge, 1947), p. 34.

29 As cited in Maggie Oman Shanon, *The Way We Pray: Celebrating Spirit Around the World* (Conari Press, Berkeley, California, USA), 2001.

30 Cited in Heather Lynn Wilson, *Blessings of a Covenant God*, Cross Books Publishing, 2012, p. 85.

References

31 Jeanne Safer, New York psychoanalyst and author of *Must We Forgive*, cited in 'The Science of Forgiveness' by Melissa Healy – *Los Angeles Times*, 6 January, 2008.

32 Temoshok, L. R. and Wald, R. L. (2005), 'Forgiveness and health in persons living with HIV/AIDS' in E. L. Worthington, Jr. (ed.), *Handbook of Forgiveness* (pp. 335-348), New York: Routledge.

33 Jina Moore. Reprinted with permission of the author. This article originally ran in *The Walrus* in May 2009. For more information, visit *www.jinamoore.com*

34 'Forgiveness: Letting go of grudges and bitterness', Mayo Clinic (7 April 2009), *www.mayoclinic.com/health/forgiveness/mh00131*

35 Tibbits, D. (2006), *Forgive to Live: How Forgiveness Can Save Your Life*, Florida Hospital, Thomas Nelson.

36 'An Essay On Criticism', 1711, part II, line 525.

37 *Stanford Forgiveness Projects Methodology: 9 Steps to Forgiveness* (Fred Luskin).

38 Toussaint, L. and Webb, J. R. (2005), 'Theoretical and empirical connections between forgiveness, mental health and well-being' in E. L. Worthington, Jr. (ed.), *Handbook of Forgiveness* (pp. 349-362), New York: Routledge.

39 Toussaint, L., 'Gender Differences in the Relationship Between Empathy and Forgiveness', *Journal of Social Psychology*, author manuscript: available in PMC 31 August 2007. Published in final edited form as *Journal of Social Psychology*, 2005, December; 145 (6): 673-685.

40 Julie H. Hall; Frank D. Fincham (2005), 'Self-Forgiveness: The Stepchild of Forgiveness Research', *Journal of Social and Clinical Psychology*, vol. 24, no. 5, pp. 621-637.

41 *www.goodreads.com/author/show/367338.Nelson_Mandela*

42 Quoted from *Lord, If I Ever Needed you, It's Now!* in Verdell Davis, *Let me Grieve, But Not Forever*, Word Publishing, 1994, p. 68.

43 *The Sermons of Mr Yorick*, vol. 1, third edition, Smith, Faulkner, Wilson and Bradley: Dublin, 1766, sermon XII, p. 252.

44 This prayer first appeared in *La Clochette*, La Ligue de la Sainte-Messe, 1912, and an English translation appeared in a 1927 issue of the Quaker magazine *Friends' Intelligencer*, where it was attributed to Saint Francis.